THE S & S HYMN BOOK
MELODY EDITION

THE S & S HYMN BOOK

Selected and edited
by
D. MAXWELL-TIMMINS

SCHOFIELD AND SIMS LIMITED
HUDDERSFIELD

0   7217   2512   0

First printed 1968
Reprinted 1969
Reprinted 1970
Reprinted 1971 (twice)
Reprinted 1972
Reprinted 1973 (twice)
Reprinted 1975 (twice)
Reprinted 1976
Reprinted 1977
Reprinted 1978
Reprinted 1979

Printed in England by
Fletcher & Son Ltd, Norwich

PREFACE

Morning assembly should be the occasion for a
corporate act of worship within the understanding
of the participants, and a stimulating religious and
musical experience. I hope this collection of hymns
will be an aid towards the fulfilment of this aim.

D. MAXWELL-TIMMINS

January, 1968

ACKNOWLEDGMENTS

The publishers and the compiler are grateful to the following for permission to include copyright material:

Oxford University Press for the hymn LORD OF ALL HOPEFULNESS, by Jan Struther from *Enlarged Songs of Praise*; for the hymn HE WHO WOULD VALIANT BE, by John Bunyan and Percy Dearmer and the tune MONKS GATE, by R. Vaughan Williams adapted from an English traditional melody from *The English Hymnal*; for the hymn O COME, O COME, EMMANUEL, translated by T. A. Lacey from *The English Hymnal*; for the hymn JESUS GOOD ABOVE ALL OTHER, by Percy Dearmer from *The English Hymnal*; for the hymn PRAISE TO THE LORD, THE ALMIGHTY, translated by C. Winkworth, altered by P. Dearmer from *The English Hymnal*; for the tune CAPEL, collected and arranged by L. E. Broadwood, harmonised by R. Vaughan Williams from *The English Hymnal*; for the tune DOWN AMPNEY, by R. Vaughan Williams from *The English Hymnal*; for the tune SINE NOMINE, by R. Vaughan Williams from *The English Hymnal*; for the tune HERONGATE, harmonised and arranged by R. Vaughan Williams from *The English Hymnal*; for the tune SHIPSTON, collected and arranged by L. E. Broadwood, harmonised by R. Vaughan Williams from *The English Hymnal*; for the tune FOREST GREEN, arranged by R. Vaughan Williams from an English traditional melody from *The English Hymnal*; for the tune KING'S WESTON, by R. Vaughan Williams from *Enlarged Songs of Praise*; for the tune WATER-END, by Geoffrey Shaw from *Enlarged Songs of Praise*; for the hymn UNTO US A BOY IS BORN, translated by Percy Dearmer from *The Oxford Book of Carols*; for the hymn THE CHURCH OF GOD A KINGDOM IS, by L. B. C. L. Muirhead from *The Yattendon Hymnal*; for the hymn JUDGE ETERNAL THRONED IN SPLENDOUR, by H. Scott Holland; for the tune WOODLANDS, by W. Greatorex; for the tune ENGLAND'S LANE, adapted by Geoffrey Shaw, from an English melody.

David Higham Associates Limited for MORNING HAS BROKEN, from *The Children's Bells*, by Eleanor Farjeon, published by Oxford University Press.

Novello and Company Limited for the tune REPTON by Sir C. Hubert H. Parry.

The Executors of the late Dr. John Ireland for the tune LOVE UNKNOWN.

J. Curwen and Sons Limited for the hymn THROUGH THE NIGHT OF DOUBT AND SORROW, and the tune MARCHING; for the hymn HILLS OF THE NORTH REJOICE, and the tune LITTLE CORNARD; for the hymn ALL CREATURES OF OUR GOD AND KING; for the tunes THAXTED, CHEERFUL and JERUSALEM.

The Trustees of the late Sir Walford Davies for the tune VISION.

Mrs. D. S. Webb, daughter of the composer, for the tune CWM RHONDDA, by the late John Hughes.

Bernard Naylor for the tune FROM STRENGTH TO STRENGTH, by the late E. W. Naylor.

A. D. Peters and Company for the hymn TURN BACK O MAN, by the late C. Bax.

Lady Arthur and Longmans, Green and Company Limited for the hymn I VOW TO THEE, MY COUNTRY, from *Poems* by Sir Cecil Spring Rice.

The Executors of Dr. Basil Harwood deceased and the Public Trustee for the tunes LUCKINGTON and THORNBURY.

CONTENTS

		Page
Preface		v
Acknowledgments		vii

Hymn No.	Title	Tune	
1	A charge to keep I have	Carlisle	1
2	A safe stronghold our God is still	Ein' Feste Burg	2
3	All hail the power of Jesu's name	Miles Lane	3
4	All people that on earth do dwell	Old Hundredth	4
5	Angel voices ever singing	Angel voices	5
6	At the name of Jesus	King's Weston	6
7	Blest are the pure in heart	Franconia	7
8	City of God, how broad and far	Richmond	8
9	Come, let us join our cheerful songs	Cheerful	9
10	Come down, O love divine (SAB)	Down Ampney	10
11	Come, ye faithful, raise the anthem (D)	Neander	12
12	Dear Lord and Father of mankind	Repton	13
13	Father, hear the prayer we offer	Gott Will's Machen	14
14	Fight the good fight with all thy might (D)	Duke Street	15
15	Fill thou my life, O Lord my God	St. Fulbert	16
16	For all the Saints who from their labours rest	Sine Nomine	17
17	For the beauty of the earth	England's Lane	18
18	Forth in thy name, O Lord, I go (SAB)	Angel's Song	19
19	Glad that I live am I	Water-End	20
20	Glorious things of thee are spoken	Austrian Hymn	21
21	God is love, his mercy brightens	Sussex	22
22	Guide me, O thou great Redeemer	Cwm Rhondda	23
23	Hail to the Lord's anointed	Cruger	24
24	He who would valiant be	Monks Gate	25
25	Hills of the North, rejoice	Little Cornard	26
26	How sweet the name of Jesus sounds (SAB)	St. Peter	27
27	Immortal, invisible, God only wise	St. Denio	28
28	In Christ there is no east or west	St. Bernard	29
29	It is a thing most wonderful	Herongate	30
30	Jesus, good above all other	Quem pastores laudavere	31
31	Jesus shall reign where'er the sun	Truro	32
32	Judge eternal, throned in splendour (D)	Rhuddlan	33
33	King of Glory, King of Peace	Gwalchmai	34

KEY TO SPECIAL TREATMENT

D — Descant provided
SAB — Arranged for Soprano, Alto, Baritone

Hymn No.	Title	Tune	Page
34	Lamb of God, I look to thee	Vienna	35
35	Lead us, heavenly Father, lead us (SAB)	Mannheim	36
36	Let all the world in every corner sing	Luckington	37
37	Lift up your hearts	Woodlands	38
38	Lord of all being, throned afar	Maryton	39
39	Lord of all hopefulness	Slane	40
40	Love divine, all loves excelling (SAB)	Love divine	41
41	Mine eyes have seen the glory	Vision	42
42	Morning has broken	Bunessan	43
43	My God, my King	Warwick	44
44	My heart and voice I raise	Ascalon	45
45	My song is love unknown	Love unknown	46
46	New every morning is the love (D)	Melcombe	47
47	Now thank we all our God	Nun Danket	48
48	O for a thousand tongues to sing	Halifax	49
49	O Jesus, I have promised	Day of Rest	50
50	O praise ye the Lord	Laudate Dominum	51
51	Onward, Christian soldiers	St. Gertrude	52
52	O worship the King	Hanover	53
53	Praise to the holiest in the height	Gerontius	54
54	Praise, my soul, the King of Heaven	Praise my soul	55
55	Praise to the Lord, the almighty	Praxis Pietatis	56
56	Rejoice, the Lord is King	Gopsal	57
57	Saviour, while my heart is tender	Shipston	58
58	Sing praise to God who reigns above	Mit Freuden Zart	59
59	Soldiers of Christ, arise	From strength to strength	60
60	Teach me, my God and King (SAB)	Sandys	61
61	The Church of God a Kingdom is	Capel	62
62	The God of Abraham praise (SAB)	Leoni	63
63	The Head that once was crowned with thorns (D)	Magnus	64
64	The King of love my shepherd is	Dominus regit me	65
65	The Lord's my shepherd	Crimond	66
66	These things shall be	Simeon	67
67	Thou whose almighty word	Moscow	68
68	Through all the changing scenes of life	Wiltshire	69
69	Through the night of doubt and sorrow	Marching	70
70	Thy hand, O God, has guided	Thornbury	71
71	Thy Kingdom come, O God (SAB)	St. Cecilia	72
72	To the name that brings salvation (D)	Oriel	73
73	Turn back, O man	Old 124th	74
74	When morning gilds the skies	Laudes Domini	75
75	Ye holy angels bright (D)	Darwall's 148th	76
76	Ye servants of God, your master proclaim	Paderborn	77

HYMNS FOR SPECIAL OCCASIONS

Hymn No.	Title	Tune	Page
	ADVENT		
77	Hark! the glad sound the Saviour comes (D)	Bristol	80
78	Lo, he comes with clouds descending	Helmsley	81
79	O come, O come, Emmanuel	Veni Emmanuel	82
	CHRISTMAS		
80	Hark! the herald angels sing	Mendelssohn	83
81	O come, all ye faithful (D)	Adeste Fideles	84
82	O little town of Bethlehem	Forest Green	85
83	Once in royal David's city (SAB)	Irby	86
84	The first Nowell	The first Nowell	88
85	Unto us a boy is born	Puer Nobis	89
86	While shepherds watched their flocks by night	Winchester Old	90
	EPIPHANY		
87	As with gladness men of old	Dix	91
88	Bethlehem, of noblest cities	Stuttgart	92
	EASTER		
89	In the cross of Christ I glory	Wychbold	93
90	Ride on, ride on in majesty	St. Drostane	94
91	There is a green hill far away	Horsley	95
92	Thine be the glory	Maccabaeus	96
93	When I survey the wondrous cross	Rockingham	97
	HARVEST		
94	All creatures of our God and King	Lasst uns Erfreuen	98
95	All things praise thee, Lord most high	Te Laudant Omnia	99
96	Come, ye thankful people, come	St. George	100
97	Praise, O praise our God and King (SAB)	Monkland	101
	NATIONAL		
98	And did those feet in ancient time	Jerusalem	102
99	I vow to thee, my country	Thaxted	103
100	Lord, while for all mankind we pray	Tallis' Ordinal	104
101	O God, our help in ages past (D)	St. Anne	105
102	The National Anthem	National Anthem	106
103	The Lord's Prayer	St. Flavian	107
	Index of first lines, arranged alphabetically		109

HYMNS WITH SPECIAL TREATMENT

DESCANTS

  11   Come, ye faithful, raise the anthem
  14   Fight the good fight
  32   Judge eternal, throned in splendour
  46   New every morning is the love
  63   The head that once was crowned with thorns
  72   To the name that brings salvation
  75   Ye holy angels bright
  77   Hark the glad sound
  81   O come, all ye faithful
101   O God, our help in ages past

ARRANGEMENT FOR SOPRANO, ALTO, BARITONE

10   Come down, O love divine
18   Forth in thy name, O Lord, I go
26   How sweet the name of Jesus sounds
35   Lead us, heavenly father, lead us
40   Love divine, all loves excelling
60   Teach me, my God and King
62   The God of Abraham praise
69   Thy Kingdom come, O God
83   Once in royal David's city
97   Praise, O praise our God and King

1
A charge to keep I have

Carlisle   C. Lockhart 1745-1815

1. A charge to keep_ I__ have, A
God to_ glo - ri - fy,__ A nev - er__ dy - ing_
soul to __ save And fit it__ for the sky.

2 To serve the present age,
My calling to fulfil;
Oh may it all my powers engage
To do my master's will.

3 Arm me with jealous care,
As in thy sight to live;
And oh thy servant, Lord, prepare
A good account to give.

4 Help me to watch and pray,
And on thyself rely;
And let me ne'er my trust betray,
But press to realms on high.

C. Wesley, 1707-1788

1

2
A safe stronghold our God is still

Ein' Feste Burg

Martin Luther 1483-1546

1. A safe strong-hold our God is still, A trust-y shield and
He'll help us clear from all the ill That hath us now o'er -

wea - pon; The an-cient prince of hell Hath
ta - ken.

risen with pur-pose fell; Strong mail of craft and power He

wear-eth in this hour; On earth is not his_ fel - low.

2 With force of arms we nothing can,
Full soon were we down-ridden;
But for us fights the proper Man,
Whom God himself hath bidden.
Ask ye 'Who is this same?'
Christ Jesus is his name,
The Lord Sabaoth's Son;
He, and no other one,
Shall conquer in the battle.

3 And were this world all devils o'er,
And watching to devour us,
We lay it not to heart so sore;
Not they can overpower us.
And let the prince of ill
Look grim as e'er he will,
He harms us not a whit;
For why?—his doom is writ;
A word shall quickly slay him.

4 God's word, for all their craft and force,
One moment will not linger,
But, spite of hell, shall have its course;
'Tis written by his finger.
And though they take our life,
Goods, honour, children, wife,
Yet is their profit small;
These things shall vanish all,
The city of God remaineth.

Martin Luther 1483-1546

3
All hail the power of Jesu's name

Miles Lane   W. Shrubsole 1760-1806

1. All hail the power of Je - su's name, Let an - gels pros-trate fall; Bring forth the roy - al di - a - dem To crown him, crown him, crown him, crown him Lord of all.

2 Crown him, ye morning stars of light
Who fixed this floating ball;
Now hail the strength of Israel's might
And crown him Lord of all.

3 Crown him, ye martyrs of our God
Who from his altar call;
Praise him whose way of pain ye trod
And crown him Lord of all.

4 Let every tribe and every tongue
To him their hearts enthral;
Lift high the universal song
And crown him Lord of all.

E. Perronet 1726-1792 and others

4
All people that on earth do dwell

Old Hundredth

From Genevan Psalter 1551

1. All peo - ple that on earth do dwell, Sing
to the Lord with cheer - ful voice; Him serve with fear, his
praise forth tell, Come ye be-fore him and re - joice.

2 The Lord ye know is God indeed,
Without our aid he did us make;
We are his folk, he doth us feed,
And for his sheep he doth us take.

3 O enter then his gates with praise,
Approach with joy his courts unto;
Praise, laud, and bless his name always,
For it is seemly so to do.

4 To Father, Son, and Holy Ghost,
The God whom heaven and earth adore,
From men and from the angel host
Be praise and glory evermore.

W. Kethe (Daye's Psalter 1560)

5
Angel voices ever singing

Angel Voices

E. G. Monk 1819-1900

1. An - gel voi - ces, ev - er sing -ing, Round thy throne of light, An - gel harps for ev - er ring - ing, Rest not day nor night; Thou - sands on - ly live to bless thee And con - fess thee Lord of might!

2 Yea, we know that thou rejoicest,
   O'er each work of thine;
   Thou didst ears and hands and voices
   For thy praise design;
   Craftsman's art and music's measure
      For thy pleasure
      All combine.

3 Thou who art beyond the farthest
   Mortal eye can scan—
   Can it be that thou regardest
   Songs of sinful man?
   Can we know that thou art near us
      And wilt hear us?
      Yea, we can.

4 In thy house, great God, we offer
   Of thine own to thee;
   And for thine acceptance proffer
   All unworthily
   Hearts and minds and hands and voices
      In our choicest
      Psalmody.

5 Honour, glory, might and merit
   Thine shall ever be,
   Father, Son, and Holy Spirit,
   Blessed Trinity!
   Of the best that thou hast given
      Earth and heaven
      Render thee.

F. Pott 1832-1909

6
At the name of Jesus

King's Weston

R. Vaughan Williams 1872-1958

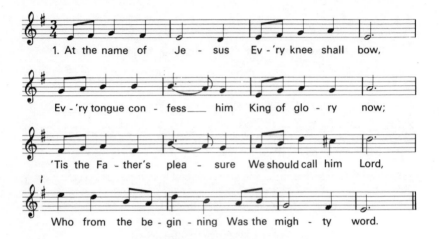

1. At the name of Je - sus Ev - 'ry knee shall bow,

Ev - 'ry tongue con - fess____ him King of glo - ry now;

'Tis the Fa - ther's plea - sure We should call him Lord,

Who from the be - gin - ning Was the migh - ty word.

2 At his voice creation
    Sprang at once to sight,
All the angel faces,
    All the hosts of light,
Thrones and dominations,
    Stars upon their way,
All the heavenly orders,
    In their great array.

3 Name him, brothers, name him,
    With love as strong as death,
But with awe and wonder,
    And with bated breath;
He is God the Saviour,
    He is Christ the Lord,
Ever to be worshipped,
    Trusted, and adored.

4 Brothers, this Lord Jesus
    Shall return again,
With his Father's glory,
    With his angel train;
For all wreaths of empire
    Meet upon his brow,
And our hearts confess him
    King of glory now.

Caroline M. Noel 1817-1877

7
Blest are the pure in heart

Franconia

W. H. Havergal 1793-1870

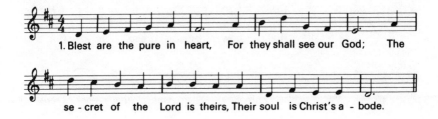

1. Blest are the pure in heart, For they shall see our God; The se - cret of the Lord is theirs, Their soul is Christ's a - bode.

2 The Lord, who left the heavens
Our life and peace to bring,
To dwell in lowliness with men,
Their pattern and their King.

3 Still to the lowly soul
He doth himself impart,
And for his dwelling and his throne
Chooseth the pure in heart.

4 Lord, we thy presence seek;
May ours this blessing be;
Give us a pure and lowly heart,
A temple meet for thee.

J. Keble 1792-1866

8
City of God, how broad and far

Richmond

S. Webbe 1740-1817
(adapted from T. Haweis 1734-1820)

1. Ci - ty of God, how broad_ and far Out -
- spread thy walls_ sub - lime! The true_ thy char - tered
free - men are Of ev - 'ry age____ and clime.

2 One holy Church, one army strong,
　　One steadfast, high intent;
　　One working band, one harvest-song,
　　One King omnipotent.

3 How purely hath thy speech come down
　　From man's primaeval youth!
　　How grandly hath thine empire grown
　　Of freedom, love and truth!

4 How gleam thy watch-fires through the night
　　With never-fainting ray!
　　How rise thy towers, serene and bright,
　　To meet the dawning day!

5 In vain the surge's angry shock,
　　In vain the drifting sands;
　　Unharmed upon the eternal Rock
　　The eternal City stands.

S. Johnson 1822-1882

9
Come, let us join our cheerful songs

Cheerful

Martin Shaw 1875-1958

1. Come, let us join our cheer - ful __ songs With an - gels round the throne; Ten thou-sand thou - sand are their tongues, But all __ their joys are one.

2 'Worthy the Lamb that died,' they cry,
  'To be exalted thus';
  'Worthy the Lamb,' our lips reply,
  'For he was slain for us.'

3 Jesus is worthy to receive
  Honour and power divine;
  And blessings more than we can give
  Be, Lord, for ever thine.

4 The whole creation join in one
  To bless the sacred name
  Of him that sits upon the throne,
  And to adore the Lamb.

Isaac Watts 1674-1748

10
Come down, O love divine

Down Ampney

R. Vaughan Williams 1872-1958

1. Come down, O love di - vine,

Seek thou this soul___ of mine, And

vis - it it with thine own ar - dour glow - ing;

O com - fort - er, draw near,

With - in my heart ap - pear, And

kin - dle it, thy ho - ly flame be - stow - ing.

2 O let it freely burn,
Till earthly passions turn
To dust and ashes, in its heat consuming:
And let thy glorious light
Shine ever on my sight,
And clothe me round, the while my path illuming.

3 And so the yearning strong,
  With which the soul will long,
  Shall far outpass the power of human telling;
  For none can guess its grace,
  Till he become the place
  Wherein the Holy Spirit makes his dwelling.

Bianco Da Siena (1434)
tr. R. F. Littledale, 1833-1890

Arrangement for Soprano, Alto, Baritone

11
Come, ye faithful, raise the anthem

Neander   J. Neander 1650-1680

1. Come, ye faith-ful, raise the an-them, Cleave the skies with shouts of praise;
Sing to him who found the ran-som, An - cient of e - ter - nal days,

God e-ter- nal, word in-car-nate, Whom the heaven of heaven o - beys.

2 Ere he raised the lofty mountains,
    . Formed the sea, or built the sky,
  Love eternal, free, and boundless,
    Forced the Lord of life to die,
  Lifted up the Prince of princes
    On the throne of Calvary.

3 Now on those eternal mountains
    Stands the sapphire throne, all bright,
  With the ceaseless alleluyas
    Which they raise, the sons of light;
  Sion's people tell his praises,
    Victor after hard-won fight.

4 Bring your harps, and bring your incense,
    Sweep the string and pour the lay;
  Let the earth proclaim his wonders,
    King of that celestial day;
  He the Lamb once slain is worthy,
    Who was dead, and lives for ay.

5 Laud and honour to the Father,
    Laud and honour to the Son,
  Laud and honour to the Spirit,
    Ever Three and ever One,
  Consubstantial, co-eternal,
    While unending ages run.

J. Hupton 1762-1849

Descant D. M-T.

12

12
Dear Lord and Father of mankind

Repton
arranged by H. A. Chambers

Sir C. Hubert H. Parry (from *"Judith"*) 1848-1918

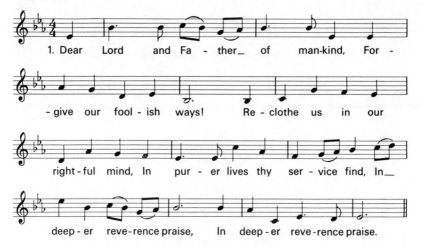

1. Dear Lord and Fa - ther_ of man-kind, For - give our fool - ish ways! Re - clothe us in our right - ful mind, In pur - er lives thy ser - vice find, In_ deep - er reve - rence praise, In deep - er reve - rence praise.

2 In simple trust like theirs who heard,
   Beside the Syrian sea,
The gracious calling of the Lord,
Let us, like them, without a word
   Rise up and follow thee.

3 O Sabbath rest by Galilee!
   O calm of hills above,
Where Jesus knelt to share with thee
The silence of eternity,
   Interpreted by love!

4 Drop thy still dews of quietness,
   Till all our strivings cease;
Take from our souls the strain and stress,
And let our ordered lives confess
   The beauty of thy peace.

5 Breathe through the heats of our desire
   Thy coolness and thy balm;
Let sense be dumb, let flesh retire;
Speak through the earthquake, wind, and fire,
   O still small voice of calm!

J. G. Whittier 1807-1892

13

13
Father, hear the prayer we offer

Gott Will's Machen

J. L. Steiner 1688-1761

1. Fa - ther, hear_ the prayer we of - fer;
Not for ease that prayer shall be, But for strength that
we may ev - er_ Live our lives cou - ra - geous-ly.

2 Not for ever in green pastures
   Do we ask our way to be;
  But the steep and rugged pathway
   May we tread rejoicingly.

3 Not for ever by still waters
   Would we idly rest and stay;
  But would smite the living fountains
   From the rocks along our way.

4 Be our strength in hours of weakness,
   In our wanderings be our guide;
  Through endeavour, failure, danger,
   Father, be thou at our side.

Mrs. L. M. Willis (1864)

14
Fight the good fight with all thy might

Duke Street

J. Hatton (d. 1793)

1. Fight the good fight with all thy might, Christ is thy strength, and Christ thy right; Lay hold on life, and it shall be Thy joy and crown e - ter - nal - ly.

2 Run the straight race through God's good grace,
    Lift up thine eyes and seek his face;
    Life with its way before us lies,
    Christ is the path, and Christ the prize.

3 Cast care aside, lean on thy guide;
    His boundless mercy will provide;
    Trust, and thy trusting soul shall prove
    Christ is its life, and Christ its love.

4 Faint not nor fear, his arms are near,
    He changeth not, and thou art dear;
    Only believe, and thou shalt see
    That Christ is all in all to thee.

J. S. B. Monsell 1811-1875

Descant   D. M-T.

15

15
Fill thou my life, O Lord my God

St. Fulbert

H. J. Gauntlett 1805-1876

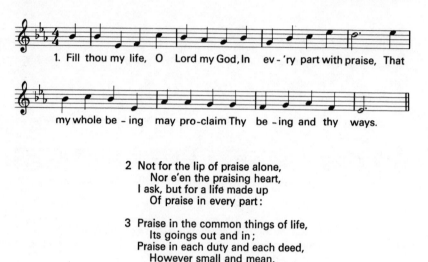

1. Fill thou my life, O Lord my God, In ev - 'ry part with praise, That my whole be - ing may pro-claim Thy be - ing and thy ways.

2 Not for the lip of praise alone,
  Nor e'en the praising heart,
I ask, but for a life made up
  Of praise in every part:

3 Praise in the common things of life,
  Its goings out and in;
Praise in each duty and each deed,
  However small and mean.

4 Fill every part of me with praise;
  Let all my being speak
Of thee and of thy love, O Lord,
  Poor though I be and weak.

5 So shall no part of day or night
  From sacredness be free;
But all my life, in every step,
  Be fellowship with thee.

H. Bonar 1808-1889

16

16
For all the Saints

Sine Nomine

R. Vaughan Williams 1872-1958

1. For all the Saints who from their la - bours rest, Who thee by faith be - fore the world con - fest, Thy name, O Je - su, be for ev - er__ blest: *Al - le - lu - ya! Al - le - lu - ya!*

2 Thou wast their rock, their fortress, and their might;
Thou, Lord, their captain in the well-fought fight;
Thou in the darkness drear their one true light:

3 O may thy soldiers, faithful, true, and bold,
Fight as the saints who nobly fought of old,
And win, with them, the victor's crown of gold:

4 And when the strife is fierce, the warfare long,
Steals on the ear the distant triumph song,
And hearts are brave again, and arms are strong:

5 But lo! there breaks a yet more glorious day;
The saints triumphant rise in bright array:
The King of glory passes on his way:

6 From earth's wide bounds, from ocean's farthest coast,
Through gates of pearl streams in the countless host,
Singing to Father, Son, and Holy Ghost.

Bishop How 1823-1897

17

17
For the beauty of the earth

England's Lane

Adapted by Geoffrey Shaw 1879-1943
from an English melody

1. For the— beau-ty of the earth, For the
beau-ty— of the skies, For the— love which from our
birth O - ver and a - round us lies: *Christ, our—*
Lord, to thee we raise This our hymn of— grate-ful praise.

2 For the beauty of each hour
    Of the day and of the night,
  Hill and vale, and tree and flower,
    Sun and moon and stars of light:

3 For the joy of ear and eye,
    For the heart and mind's delight,
  For the mystic harmony
    Linking sense to sound and sight:

4 For the joy of human love,
    Brother, sister, parent, child,
  Friends on earth, and friends above,
    For all gentle thoughts and mild.

5 For each perfect gift of thine
    To our race so freely given,
  Graces human and divine,
    Flowers of earth and buds of heaven:

F. S. Pierpoint 1835-1917

18

18
Forth in thy name, O Lord, I go

Angel's Song

Orlando Gibbons 1583-1625

1. Forth in thy name, O Lord, I go, My dai - ly la - bour to pur - sue: Thee, on - ly thee, re - solved to know, In all I think, or speak, or do.

2 Thee may I set at my right hand,
Whose eyes my inmost substance see,
And labour on at thy command,
And offer all my works to thee.

3 Give me to bear thy easy yoke,
And every moment watch and pray,
And still to things eternal look,
And hasten to thy glorious day—

4 For thee delightfully employ
Whate'er thy bounteous grace hath given,
And run my course with even joy,
And closely walk with thee to heaven.

C. Wesley 1707-1788

Arrangement for Soprano, Alto, Baritone

19

19
Glad that I live am I

Water-End

Geoffrey Shaw 1879-1943

1. Glad that I live am I That the sky is blue;

Glad for the coun - try lanes And the fall of dew.

2. Af - ter the sun, the rain, Af - ter the rain, the sun;

This is the way of life, Till the work be done.

3. All that we need to do, Be we low or high, Is to

see that we grow Near - er the sky.

L. W. Reese 1856-1935

20
Glorious things of thee are spoken

Austrian Hymn   F. J. Haydn 1732-1809

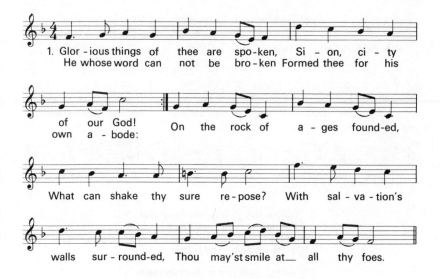

1. Glor - ious things of thee are spo-ken, Si - on, ci - ty
   He whose word can not be bro-ken Formed thee for his

   of our God! On the rock of a - ges found-ed,
   own a - bode:

   What can shake thy sure re-pose? With sal - va - tion's

   walls sur - round-ed, Thou may'st smile at— all thy foes.

2 See, the streams of living waters,
    Springing from eternal love,
  Well supply thy sons and daughters,
    And all fear of want remove:
  Who can faint while such a river
    Ever flows their thirst to assuage?
  Grace, which like the Lord the giver,
    Never fails from age to age.

3 Saviour, if of Sion's city
    I, through grace, a member am,
  Let the world deride or pity,
    I will glory in thy name:
  Fading is the worldling's pleasure,
    All his boasted pomp and show;
  Solid joys and lasting treasure
    None but Sion's children know.

J. Newton 1725-1807

21

21
God is love, his mercy brightens

Sussex

English traditional melody

1. God is love, his mer - cy___ bright - ens
All the path in which we rove; Bliss he wakes, and
woe he light-ens: God is wis - dom, God is love.

2 Chance and change are busy ever:
   Man decays, and ages move;
   But his mercy waneth never:
   God is wisdom, God is love.

3 E'en the hour that darkest seemeth
   Will his changeless goodness prove;
   From the gloom his brightness streameth:
   God is wisdom, God is love.

4 He with earthly cares entwineth
   Hope and comfort from above;
   Everywhere his glory shineth:
   God is wisdom, God is love.

John Bowring 1792-1872

22
Guide me, O thou great redeemer

Cwm Rhondda

John Hughes 1873-1932

1. Guide me, O thou great re - deem-er, Pil - grim through this
bar - ren land; I am weak, but thou_ art _ migh - ty,
Hold me with thy_ power - ful hand. Bread of hea - ven,
bread of hea - ven, Feed me now and ev - er
more, feed me now_ and_ ev - er - more.

2 Open thou the crystal fountain
Whence the healing stream shall flow,
Let the fiery, cloudy pillars
Lead me all my journey through.
Strong deliverer, be thou still my strength and shield.

3 When I tread the verge of Jordan
Bid my anxious fears subside,
Death of deaths, and hell's destruction,
Land me safe on Canaan's side.
Songs of praises, I will ever sing to thee.

W. Williams 1717-1791

23

23
Hail to the Lord's anointed

Cruger

J. Cruger 1598-1662, ad. Monk

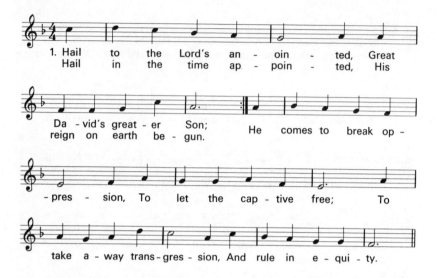

1. Hail to the Lord's an - oin - ted, Great
   Da - vid's great - er Son; He comes to break op -
   - pres - sion, To let the cap - tive free; To
   take a - way trans - gres - sion, And rule in e - qui - ty.

Hail in the time ap - poin - ted, His
reign on earth be - gun.

2 He comes, with succour speedy,
  To those who suffer wrong;
  To help the poor and needy,
  And bid the weak be strong;
  To give them songs for sighing,
  Their darkness turn to light,
  Whose souls, condemned and dying,
  Were precious in his sight.

3 He shall come down like showers,
  Upon the fruitful earth;
  Love, joy and hope, like flowers,
  Spring in his path to birth;
  Before him on the mountains,
  Shall peace the herald go;
  And righteousness in fountains
  From hill to valley flow.

4 Kings shall fall down before him,
  And gold and incense bring;
  All nations shall adore him,
  His praise all people sing;
  For him shall prayer unceasing
  And daily vows ascend;
  His kingdom still increasing,
  A kingdom without end.

5 O'er every foe victorious,
  He on his throne shall rest,
  From age to age more glorious,
  All-blessing and all-blest.
  The tide of time shall never
  His covenant remove;
  His name shall stand for ever,
  His changeless name of love.

J. Montgomery 1771-1854

24
He who would valiant be

Monks Gate

R. Vaughan Williams 1872-1958
adapted from an English traditional melody

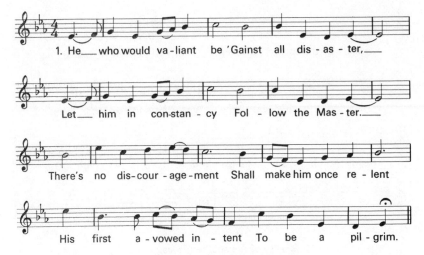

1. He__ who would va - liant be 'Gainst all dis - as - ter,__
Let__ him in con-stan - cy Fol - low the Mas - ter.__
There's no dis-cour - age-ment Shall make him once re - lent
His first a - vowed in - tent To be a pil - grim.

2 Who so beset him round
  With dismal stories,
  Do but themselves confound—
      His strength the more is.
  No foes shall stay his might,
  Though he with giants fight:
  He will make good his right
      To be a pilgrim.

3 Since, Lord, thou dost defend
  Us with thy Spirit,
  We know we at the end
      Shall life inherit.
  Then fancies flee away!
  I'll fear not what men say,
  I'll labour night and day
      To be a pilgrim.

Percy Dearmer 1867-1936
after John Bunyan 1628-1688

25
Hills of the north, rejoice

Little Cornard

Martin Shaw 1875-1958

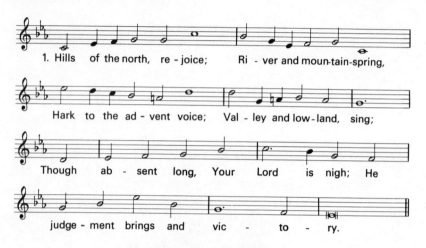

1. Hills of the north, re - joice; Ri - ver and moun-tain-spring,
Hark to the ad - vent voice; Val - ley and low - land, sing;
Though ab - sent long, Your Lord is nigh; He
judge - ment brings and vic - to - ry.

2 Isles of the southern seas,
    Deep in your coral caves
Pent be each warring breeze.
    Lulled be your restless waves:
He comes to reign with boundless sway,
And makes your wastes his great highway.

3 Lands of the east, awake,
    Soon shall your sons be free;
The sleep of ages break,
    And rise to liberty.
On your far hills, long cold and grey,
Has dawned the everlasting day.

4 Shores of the utmost west,
    Ye that have waited long,
Unvisited, unblest,
    Break forth to swelling song;
High raise the note, that Jesus died,
Yet lives and reigns, the crucified.

5 Shout, while ye journey home;
    Songs be in every mouth;
Lo, from the north we come,
    From east, and west, and south.
City of God, the bond are free,
We come to live and reign in thee!

Charles E. Oakley 1832-1865

26
How sweet the name of Jesus sounds

St. Peter   A. R. Reinagle 1799-1877

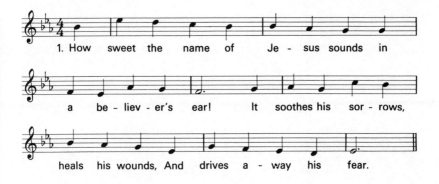

1. How sweet the name of Je - sus sounds in a be - liev - er's ear! It soothes his sor - rows, heals his wounds, And drives a - way his fear.

2 It makes the wounded spirit whole,
    And calms the troubled breast;
'Tis manna to the hungry soul,
    And to the weary rest.

3 Dear name! the rock on which I build,
    My shield and hiding-place,
My never-failing treasury fill'd
    With boundless stores of grace.

4 Weak is the effort of my heart,
    And cold my warmest thought;
But when I see thee as thou art,
    I'll praise thee as I ought.

5 Till then I would thy love proclaim
    With every fleeting breath:
And may the music of thy name
    Refresh my soul in death.

J. Newton 1725-1807

Arrangement for Soprano, Alto, Baritone

27
Immortal, invisible, God only wise

St. Denio

Welsh Hymn melody

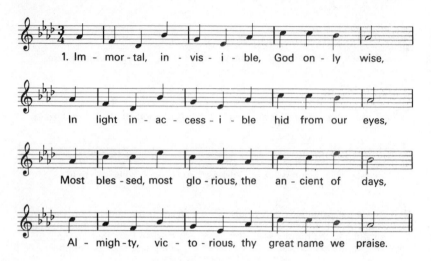

1. Im - mor - tal, in - vis - i - ble, God on - ly wise,

In light in - ac - cess - i - ble hid from our eyes,

Most bles - sed, most glo - rious, the an - cient of days,

Al - migh - ty, vic - to - rious, thy great name we praise.

2 Unresting, unhasting, and silent as light,
Nor wanting, nor wasting, thou rulest in might;
Thy justice like mountains high soaring above,
Thy clouds which are fountains of goodness and love.

3 To all life thou givest—to both great and small;
In all life thou livest, the true life of all;
We blossom and flourish as leaves on the tree,
And wither and perish—but nought changeth thee.

4 Great Father of glory, pure Father of light,
Thine angels adore thee, all veiling their sight;
All laud we would render: O help us to see
'Tis only the splendour of light hideth thee.

W. C. Smith 1824-1908

28
In Christ there is no east or west

St. Bernard

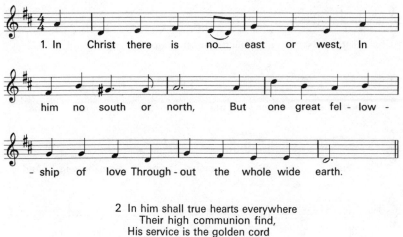

ad. *Tochter Sion* 1741

1. In Christ there is no east or west, In him no south or north, But one great fel-low-ship of love Through-out the whole wide earth.

2 In him shall true hearts everywhere
   Their high communion find,
   His service is the golden cord
   Close-binding all mankind.

3 Join hands, then, brothers of the faith,
   Whate'er your race may be!
   Who serves my Father as a son
   Is surely kin to me.

4 In Christ now meet both east and west,
   In him meet south and north,
   All Christly souls are one in him,
   Throughout the whole wide earth.

John Oxenham 1852-1941

29

29
It is a thing most wonderful

Herongate

English traditional melody
Harmonised and arranged by R. Vaughan Williams 1872-1958

1. It is a thing most won - der - ful, Al - most too won - der - ful__ to be, That God's_ own Son__ should come_ from heaven, And die to save a child__ like me.

2 And yet I know that it is true :
   He came to this poor world below,
And wept, and toiled, and mourned, and died,
   Only because he loved us so.

3 I cannot tell how he could love
   A child so weak and full of sin ;
His love must be most wonderful,
   If he could die my love to win.

4 It is most wonderful to know
   His love for me so free and sure ;
To guide and help me on life's way,
   A love for ever to endure.

5 And so I want to love thee, Lord ;
   O light the flame within my heart,
And I will love thee more and more,
   Until I see thee as thou art.

Bishop How 1823-1897

30
Jesus, good above all other

Quem Pastores Laudavere

14th Century German

1. Je - sus, good a - bove__ all o - ther,
Gen - tle child__ of gen - tle mo - ther,
In a sta - ble born our bro - ther,
Give us grace__ to per - se - vere.

2 Jesus, cradled in a manger,
For us facing every danger,
Living as a homeless stranger,
   Make we thee our King most dear.

3 Jesus, for thy people dying,
Risen Master, death defying,
Lord in heaven, thy grace supplying,
   Keep us to thy presence near.

4 Jesus, who our sorrows bearest,
All our thoughts and hopes thou sharest,
Thou to man the truth declarest;
   Help us all thy truth to hear.

5 Lord, in all our doings guide us;
Pride and hate shall ne'er divide us;
We'll go on with thee beside us,
   And with joy we'll persevere!

Percy Dearmer 1867-1936

31
Jesus shall reign where'er the sun

Truro

Psalmodia Evangelica 1789

1. Je - sus shall reign where - 'er the sun Does his suc - ces - sive_ journ- eys run; His King-dom stretch from shore to_ shore Till moons shall wax and wane no more.

2 People and realms of every tongue
   Dwell on his love with sweetest song,
   And infant voices shall proclaim
   Their early blessings on his name.

3 Let every creature rise and bring
   Peculiar honours to our King;
   Angels descend with songs again,
   And earth repeat the long amen.

Isaac Watts 1674-1748

32
Judge eternal, throned in splendour

Rhuddlan   Welsh traditional melody

1. Judge e - ter - nal, throned in splen - dour,
   With thy liv - ing fire of judge - ment

Lord of lords and King of kings, So - lace all___ its
Purge this realm of bit - ter things:

wide do - min - ion With the heal - ing of thy wings.

2 Still the weary folk are pining
   For the hour that brings release:
   And the city's crowded clangour
   Cries aloud for sin to cease;
   And the homesteads and the woodlands
   Plead in silence for their peace.

3 Crown, O God, thine own endeavour:
   Cleave our darkness with thy sword:
   Feed the faint and hungry heathen
   With the richness of thy Word:
   Cleanse the body of this empire
   Through the glory of the Lord.

H. S. Holland 1847-1918

Descant   D. M-T.

33

33
King of glory, King of peace

Gwalchmai

J. D. Jones 1827-1870

1. King of glor-y,— King of peace, I will love thee;
And that love may_ nev-er cease, I will move thee.
Thou hast grant-ed my re-quest, Thou hast heard_ me:
Thou didst note my_ work-ing breast, Thou hast spared me.

2 Wherefore with my utmost art
    I will sing thee,
And the cream of all my heart
    I will bring thee.
Though my sins against me cried,
    Thou didst clear me;
And alone, when they replied,
    Thou didst hear me.

3 Seven whole days, not one in seven,
    I will praise thee;
In my heart, though not in heaven,
    I can raise thee.
Small it is, in this poor sort
    To enrol thee:
E'en eternity's too short
    To extol thee.

George Herbert 1593-1632

34

34
Lamb of God, I look to thee

Vienna

J. H. Knecht 1752-1817

1. Lamb of God, I look to thee,
Thou shalt my ex - am - ple be: Thou art gen - tle,
meek, and mild, Thou wast once a lit - tle child.

2 Fain I would be as thou art;
Give me thy obedient heart;
Thou art pitiful and kind,
Let me have thy loving mind.

3 Meek and lowly may I be;
Thou art all humility;
Let me to my betters bow,
Subject to thy parents thou.

4 Let me above all fulfil
God my heavenly father's will;
Never his good spirit grieve,
Only to his glory live.

5 I shall then show forth thy praise,
Serve thee all my happy days;
Then the world shall always see
Christ, the holy child, in me.

C. Wesley 1707-1788

35
Lead us, heavenly Father, lead us

Mannheim   F. Filitz 1804-1876

1. Lead us, heav'n-ly Fa-ther, lead us O'er the world's tem-
- pes-tuous sea; Guard us, guide us, keep us, feed us,
For we have no help but thee; Yet pos-sess-ing
ev-'ry bless-ing If our God our Fa-ther be.

2 Saviour, breathe forgiveness o'er us;
　　All our weakness thou dost know,
　Thou didst tread this earth before us,
　　Thou didst feel its keenest woe;
　Lone and dreary, faint and weary,
　　Through the desert thou didst go.

3 Spirit of our God, descending,
　　Fill our hearts with heavenly joy,
　Love with every passion blending,
　　Pleasure that can never cloy:
　Thus provided, pardoned, guided,
　　Nothing can our peace destroy.

J. Edmeston 1791-1867

Arrangement for Soprano, Alto, Baritone

36

36
Let all the world in every corner sing

Luckington   Basil Harwood 1859-1949

1. Let all the world in ev - 'ry cor - ner sing: My God and King! The heav'ns are not too high, His praise may thi - ther fly; The earth is not too low, His prais - es there may grow. Let all the world in ev - 'ry cor - ner sing: My God and King!

2 Let all the world in every corner sing:
   My God and King!
   The Church with psalms must shout,
   No door can keep them out;
   But, above all, the heart
   Must bear the longest part.
   Let all the world in every corner sing:
   My God and King!

George Herbert 1593-1633

37
Lift up your hearts

Woodlands   W. Greatorex 1877-1949

1. "Lift up your hearts!" We lift them,_ Lord, to
thee; Here at thy feet none o - ther may we
see: Lift up your hearts, e'en so with one ac - cord, We
lift them up, we lift them to the Lord.

2 Above the level of the former years,
The mire of sin, the slough of guilty fears,
The mist of doubt, the blight of love's decay,
O Lord of light, lift all our hearts today.

3 Above the swamps of subterfuge and shame,
The deeds, the thoughts that honour may not name,
The halting tongue that dares not tell the whole,
O Lord of truth, lift every Christian soul.

4 Lift every gift that thou thyself hast given;
Low lies the best till lifted up to heaven;
Low lie the bounding heart, the teeming brain,
Till, sent from God, they mount to God again.

5 Then, as the trumpet-call, in after years,
'Lift up your hearts,' rings pealing in our ears,
Still shall those hearts respond, with full accord:
'We lift them up, we lift them to the Lord.'

H. M. Butler 1833-1918

38
Lord of all being, throned afar

Maryton

H. P. Smith 1825-1898

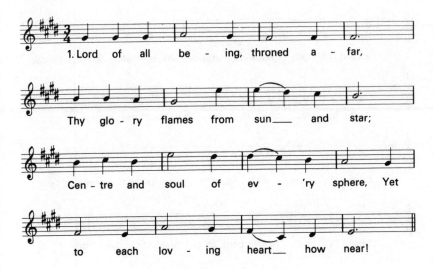

1. Lord of all be - ing, throned a - far,

Thy glo - ry flames from sun___ and star;

Cen - tre and soul of ev - 'ry sphere, Yet

to each lov - ing heart___ how near!

2 Sun of our life, thy quickening ray
  Sheds on our path the glow of day;
  Star of our hope, thy softened light
  Cheers the long watches of the night.

3 Our midnight is thy smile withdrawn;
  Our noontide is thy gracious dawn;
  Our rainbow arch, thy mercy's sign;
  All, save the clouds of sin, are thine.

4 Lord of all life, below, above,
  Whose light is truth, whose warmth is love,
  Before thy ever-blazing throne
  We ask no lustre of our own.

5 Grant us thy truth to make us free,
  And kindling hearts that burn for thee,
  Till all thy living altars claim
  One holy light, one heavenly flame.

O. W. Holmes 1809-1894

39

39
Lord of all hopefulness

Slane

Irish traditional melody

1. Lord of all__ hope-ful-ness, Lord of all joy, Whose trust, ev-er child like, no cares could des-troy, Be there at__ our__ wak-ing, and give us, we pray, Your bliss in our hearts, Lord, at the break of the day.

2 Lord of all eagerness, Lord of all faith,
  Whose strong hands were skilled at the plane and the lathe,
  Be there at our labours, and give us, we pray,
  Your strength in our hearts, Lord, at the noon of the day.

3 Lord of all kindliness, Lord of all grace,
  Your hands swift to welcome, your arms to embrace,
  Be there at our homing, and give us, we pray,
  Your love in our hearts, Lord, at the eve of the day.

4 Lord of all gentleness, Lord of all calm,
  Whose voice is contentment, whose presence is balm,
  Be there at our sleeping, and give us, we pray,
  Your peace in our hearts, Lord, at the end of the day.

Jan Struther 1901-1953

40
Love Divine, all loves excelling

Love Divine

Sir John Stainer 1840-1901

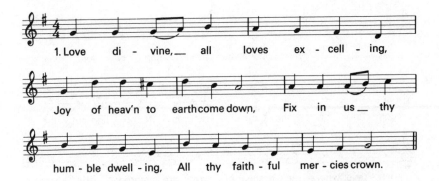

1. Love di - vine,— all loves ex - cell - ing,
Joy of heav'n to earth come down, Fix in us — thy
hum - ble dwell - ing, All thy faith - ful mer - cies crown.

2 Jesu, thou art all compassion,
    Pure unbounded love thou art;
Visit us with thy salvation,
    Enter every trembling heart.

3 Come, almighty to deliver,
    Let us all thy grace receive;
Suddenly return, and never,
    Never more thy temples leave.

4 Thee we would be always blessing,
    Serve thee as thy hosts above;
Pray, and praise thee, without ceasing,
    Glory in thy perfect love.

5 Finish then thy new creation,
    Pure and spotless let us be;
Let us see thy great salvation,
    Perfectly restored in thee;

6 Changed from glory into glory,
    Till in heav'n we take our place,
Till we cast our crowns before thee,
    Lost in wonder, love, and praise.

C. Wesley 1707-1788

Arrangement for Soprano, Alto, Baritone

41
Mine eyes have seen the glory

Vision

Sir H. Walford Davies 1869-1941

1. Mine___ eyes have seen the glo - ry of the
com - ing of the Lord; He is tramp - ling out the
vin - tage where the grapes of wrath are stored; He hath
loosed the fate - ful light-ning of his ter - ri - ble swift
sword; His___ truth is march - ing on.___

2 He hath sounded forth the trumpet that shall never call retreat;
He is sifting out the hearts of men before his judgement seat.
O be swift, my soul, to answer him; be jubilant, my feet!
Our God is marching on.

J. W. Howe 1819-1910

42
Morning has broken

Bunessan

Old Gaelic melody

1. Morn-ing has bro - ken   Like the first morn - ing,

Black-bird has spok - en,   Like the first bird.____

Praise for the sing - ing!   Praise for the morn - ing!

Praise for them, spring - ing   Fresh from the word.____

2 Sweet the rain's new fall
  Sunlit from heaven,
  Like the first dewfall
  On the first grass.
        Praise for the sweetness
        Of the wet garden,
        Sprung in completeness
        Where his feet pass.

3 Mine is the sunlight!
  Mine is the morning
  Born of the one light
  Eden saw play!
        Praise with elation,
        Praise every morning,
        God's recreation
        Of the new day!

Eleanor Farjeon 1881-1965

43

43
My God, my King

Warwick

S. Stanley 1767-1822

1. My God, my King, Thy praise I sing, My heart is all thine own; My high - est powers, My choic - est hours, I yield to thee a - lone.

2 My voice awake,
Thy part to take,
My soul the concert join;
Till all around
Shall catch the sound,
And mix their hymns with mine.

3 But man is weak
Thy praise to speak;
Your God, ye angels, sing;
'Tis yours to see,
More near than we,
The glories of our King.

4 His truth and grace
Fill time and space;
As large his honours be,
Till all that live
Their homage give,
And praise my God with me.

H. F. Lyte 1793-1847

44
My heart and voice I raise

Ascalon   Silesian Folk Song

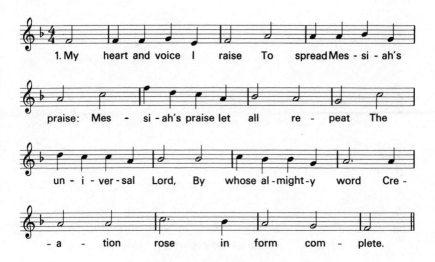

1. My heart and voice I raise To spread Mes - si - ah's praise: Mes - si - ah's praise let all re - peat The un - i - ver - sal Lord, By whose al - might - y word Cre - a - tion rose in form com - plete.

2 With mercy's mildest grace
He governs all our race
In wisdom, righteousness and love;
Who to Messiah fly
Shall find redemption nigh,
And all his great salvation prove.

3 Hail, Saviour, Prince of Peace!
Thy Kingdom shall increase
Till all the world thy glory see;
And righteousness abound,
As the great deep profound,
And fill the earth with purity.

B. Rhodes 1743-1815

45
My song is love unknown

Love unknown

John Ireland 1879-1962

1. My song is love un - known, My Sav-iour's love to
me, Love to the love - less shown, That they might
love - ly be. O who am I, That
for my sake, My Lord should take Frail flesh and die?

2 He came from his blest throne
  Salvation to bestow;
  But men made strange, and none .
  The longed-for Christ would know.
    But O my friend,
    My friend indeed,
    Who at my need
    His life did spend!

3 Sometimes they strew his way,
  And his sweet praises sing;
  Resounding all the day
  Hosannas to their King.
    Then: 'Crucify!'
    Is all their breath,
    And for his death
    They thirst and cry.

4 Here might I stay and sing,
  No story so divine,
  Never was love, dear King,
  Never was grief like thine.
    This is my friend,
    In whose sweet praise
    I all my days
    Could gladly spend.

S. Crossman 1624-1683

46
New every morning is the love

Melcombe

S. Webbe 1740-1816

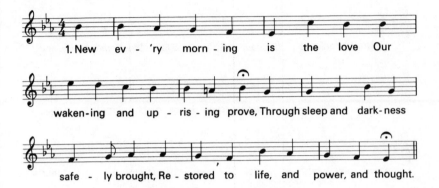

1. New ev - 'ry morn - ing is the love Our

waken-ing and up - ris - ing prove, Through sleep and dark-ness

safe - ly brought, Re - stored to life, and power, and thought.

2 New mercies, each returning day,
  Hover around us while we pray;
  New perils past, new sins forgiven,
  New thoughts of God, new hopes of heaven.

3 The trivial round, the common task,
  Would furnish all we ought to ask,—
  Room to deny ourselves, a road
  To bring us daily nearer God.

4 Only, O Lord, in thy dear love
  Fit us for perfect rest above;
  And help us this and every day
  To live more nearly as we pray.

J. Keble 1792-1866

Descant Martin Shaw 1875-1958

47
Now thank we all our God

Nun Danket

J. Crüger 1598-1662

1. Now thank we all our God With heart and hands and

voi - ces; Who won - drous things hath done, In

whom his world re - joi - ces; Who from our mo - ther's

arms, Hath blessed us on our way With

count - less gifts of love, ' And still is ours to - day.

2   O may this bounteous God
Through all our life be near us,
    With ever-joyful hearts
And blessed peace to cheer us,
    And keep us in his grace,
      And guide us when perplexed,
    And free us from all ills
      In this world and the next.

3   All praise and thanks to God
The Father now be given,
    The Son, and him who reigns
With them in highest heaven,
    The one eternal God,
      Whom earth and heaven adore;
    For thus it was, is now,
      And shall be evermore.

M. Rinkhart 1586-1649, Tr. C. Winkworth

48
O for a thousand tongues to sing

Halifax

D. Maxwell-Timmins

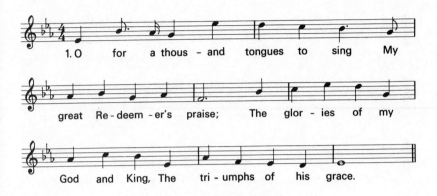

1. O for a thous - and tongues to sing My great Re - deem - er's praise; The glor - ies of my God and King, The tri - umphs of his grace.

2 Jesus the name that charms our fears,
   That bids our sorrows cease;
   'Tis music in the sinner's ears,
   'Tis life, and health, and peace.

3 He speaks, and, listening to his voice,
   New life the dead receive;
   The mournful, broken hearts rejoice,
   The humble poor believe.

4 Hear him, ye deaf; his praise, ye dumb,
   Your loosened tongues employ;
   Ye blind, behold your Saviour come;
   And leap, ye lame, for joy!

5 My gracious Master and my God,
   Assist me to proclaim,
   To spread through all the earth abroad
   The honours of thy name.

C. Wesley 1707-1788

49

49
O Jesus, I have promised

Day of rest

J. W. Elliott 1833-1915

1. O Je-sus, I have prom-ised To serve thee_ to the
end; Be thou for ev-er__ near me, My
mas-ter and my friend; I shall not fear the
bat-tle If thou art by my side, Nor__
wan-der from the path-way, If thou wilt_ be my guide.

2 O let me feel thee near me:
   The world is ever near;
I see the sights that dazzle,
   The tempting sounds I hear;
My foes are ever near me,
   Around me and within;
But, Jesus, draw thou nearer,
   And shield my soul from sin.

3 O let me hear thee speaking
   In accents clear and still,
Above the storms of passion,
   The murmurs of self-will;
O speak to reassure me,
   To hasten or control;
O speak, and make me listen,
   Thou guardian of my soul.

4 O Jesus, thou hast promised
   To all who follow thee,
That where thou art in glory
   There shall thy servant be;
And, Jesus, I have promised
   To serve thee to the end;
O give me grace to follow,
   My master and my friend.

J. E. Bode 1816-1874

50
O praise ye the Lord

Laudate Dominum

Sir C. Hubert H. Parry 1848-1918

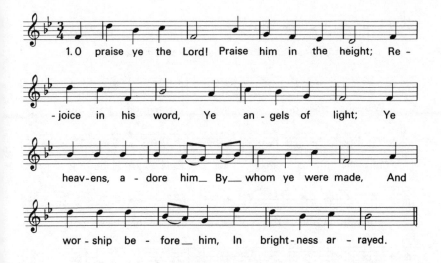

1. O praise ye the Lord! Praise him in the height; Re-joice in his word, Ye an-gels of light; Ye heav-ens, a-dore him_ By_ whom ye were made, And wor-ship be-fore_ him, In bright-ness ar-rayed.

2 O praise ye the Lord!
    Praise him upon earth,
In tuneful accord,
    Ye sons of new birth;
Praise him who hath brought you
    His grace from above,
Praise him who hath taught you
    To sing of his love.

3 O praise ye the Lord!
    All things that give sound;
Each jubilant chord,
    Re-echo around;
Loud organs, his glory
    Forth tell in deep tone,
And sweet harp, the story
    Of what he hath done.

4 O praise ye the Lord!
    Thanksgiving and song
To him be outpour'd
    All ages along:
For love in creation,
    For heaven restored,
For grace of salvation,
    O praise ye the Lord!

Sir H. W. Baker 1821-1877

51
Onward, Christian soldiers

St. Gertrude   Sir A. S. Sullivan 1842-1900

1. On-ward, Christ-ian sol - diers, March-ing as to war,
With the cross of Je - sus Go - ing on be - fore.
Christ the roy - al mas - ter Leads a - gainst the foe;
For-ward in - to bat - tle,__ See, his ban-ners go!
On - ward, Christ-ian sol - diers,_ March-ing as to__ war,
With the cross of Je - sus - Go - ing on be - fore.

2 At the sign of triumph
   Satan's host doth flee;
On then, Christian soldiers,
   On to victory!
Hell's foundations quiver
   At the shout of praise;
Brothers, lift your voices,
   Loud your anthems raise:

3 Like a mighty army
   Moves the Church of God;
Brothers, we are treading
   Where the Saints have trod.
We are not divided,
   All one body we,
One in hope and doctrine,
   One in charity:

4 Crowns and thrones may perish,
   Kingdoms rise and wane,
But the Church of Jesus
   Constant will remain.
Gates of hell can never
   'Gainst that Church prevail;
We have Christ's own promise,
   And that cannot fail:

5 Onward, then, ye people!
   Join our happy throng;
Blend with ours your voices
   In the triumph song;
"Glory, laud, and honour,
   Unto Christ the King!"
This through countless ages
   Men and angels sing:

S. Baring Gould 1834-1924

52
O worship the King

Hanover   Dr. W. Croft 1678-1727

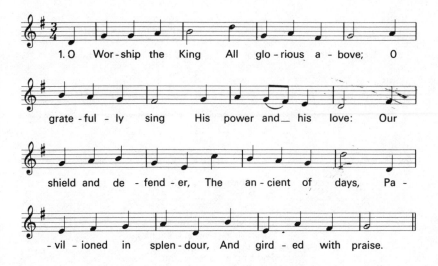

1. O Wor-ship the King All glo-rious a - bove; O
grate - ful - ly sing His power and __ his love: Our
shield and de - fend - er, The an - cient of days, Pa -
- vil – ioned in splen - dour, And gird - ed with praise.

2 O tell of his might,
    O sing of his grace,
Whose robe is the light,
    Whose canopy space.
His chariots of wrath
    The deep thunder-clouds form,
And dark is his path
    On the wings of the storm..

3 This earth, with its store
    Of wonders untold,
Almighty, thy power
    Hath founded of old;
Hath stablished it fast
    By a changeless decree,
And round it hath cast,
    Like a mantle, the sea.

4 Thy bountiful care
    What tongue can recite?
It breathes in the air,
    It shines in the light;
It streams from the hills,
    It descends to the plain,
And sweetly distils
    In the dew and the rain.

5 O measureless might,
    Ineffable love,
While angels delight
    To hymn thee above,
Thy humbler creation,
    Though feeble their lays,
With true adoration
    Shall sing to thy praise.

Sir R. Grant 1779-1838

53
Praise to the Holiest in the height

Gerontius

J. B. Dykes 1823-1876

1. Praise to the Hol - iest in the height,
And in the depth be praise; In all his words most
won - der - ful, Most sure in all his ways.

2 O loving wisdom of our God!
   When all was sin and shame,
   A second Adam to the fight
   And to the rescue came.

3 O wisest love! that flesh and blood,
   Which did in Adam fail,
   Should strive afresh against the foe,
   Should strive and should prevail;

4 And that a higher gift than grace
   Should flesh and blood refine.
   God's presence and his very Self,
   And essence all-divine.

5 O generous love! that he, who smote
   In man for man the foe,
   The double agony in man
   For man should undergo;

6 And in the garden secretly,
   And on the cross on high,
   Should teach his brethren, and inspire
   To suffer and to die.

7 Praise to the Holiest in the height,
   And in the depth be praise;
   In all his words most wonderful,
   Most sure in all his ways.

Cardinal Newman 1801-1890

54
Praise, my soul, the King of heaven

Praise my soul

J. Goss 1800-1880

1. Praise, my soul, the King of hea - ven;
To his feet thy tri - bute bring; Ran - somed,
healed, re - stored, for - giv - en, Who like me his
praise should sing? Praise him! Praise him! Praise him!
Praise him! Praise the ev - er - last - ing King.

2 Praise him for his grace and favour
   To our fathers in distress;
   Praise him still the same forever,
   Slow to chide, and swift to bless.
   Praise him! Praise him!
   Praise him! Praise him!
   Glorious in his faithfulness.

3 Father-like, he tends and spares us;
   Well our feeble frame he knows;
   In his hands he gently bears us,
   Rescues us from all our foes.
   Praise him! Praise him!
   Praise him! Praise him!
   Widely as his mercy flows.

4 Angels, help us to adore him;
   Ye behold him face to face;
   Sun and moon bow down before him,
   Dwellers all in time and space.
   Praise him! Praise him!
   Praise him! Praise him!
   Praise with us the God of grace.

H. F. Lyte 1793-1847

55
Praise to the Lord, the Almighty

Praxis Pietatis

Sohr's edition 1668

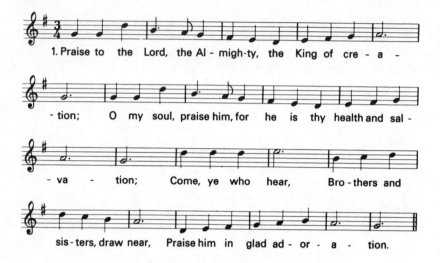

1. Praise to the Lord, the Al - migh-ty, the King of cre - a - tion; O my soul, praise him, for he is thy health and sal - va - tion; Come, ye who hear, Bro - thers and sis - ters, draw near, Praise him in glad ad - or - a - tion.

2 Praise to the Lord, who doth prosper thy work and defend thee;
Surely his goodness and mercy here daily attend thee;
  Ponder anew
  All the Almighty can do,
He who with love doth befriend thee.

3 Praise to the Lord! O let all that is in me adore him!
All that hath life and breath come now with praises before him!
  Let the amen
  Sound from his people again;
Gladly for ay we adore him!

J. Neander 1650-1686, Tr. C. Winkworth 1827-1878 and P. Dearmer 1867-1936

56
Rejoice, the Lord is King

Gopsal

G. F. Handel 1685-1759

1. Re - joice, the Lord is King, Your Lord and_ King a -
- dore; Mor - tals, give thanks and sing, And
tri - umph ev - er - more: Lift up your heart, lift
up your voice; Re - joice, a - gain I __ say, re - joice.

2 Jesus the Saviour reigns,
    The God of truth and love:
When he had purged our stains,
    He took his seat above:
Lift up your heart, lift up your voice;
Rejoice, again I say, rejoice.

3 He sits at God's right hand,
    Till all his foes submit,
And bow to his command,
    And fall beneath his feet:
Lift up your heart, lift up your voice;
Rejoice, again I say, rejoice.

4 His kingdom cannot fail;
    He rules o'er earth and heav'n;
The keys of death and hell
    Are to our Jesus given:
Lift up your heart, lift up your voice;
Rejoice, again I say, rejoice.

C. Wesley 1707-1788

57
Saviour, while my heart is tender

Shipston

English traditional melody
Collected and arranged by L. E. Broadwood 1858-1929
Harmonised by R. Vaughan Williams 1872-1958

1. Sav - iour, while my heart is ten - der,
I would yield that heart to thee, All my powers to
thee sur-ren - der, Thine, and on - ly thine, to be.

2 Take me now, Lord Jesus, take me;
   Let my youthful heart be thine;
   Thy devoted servant make me;
   Fill my soul with love divine.

3 Send me, Lord, where thou wilt send me,
   Only do thou guide my way;
   May thy grace through life attend me,
   Gladly then shall I obey.

4 Thine I am, O Lord, for ever,
   To thy service set apart;
   Suffer me to leave thee never;
   Seal thine image on my heart.

J. Burton 1803-1877

58
Sing praise to God who reigns above

Mit Freuden Zart

Kirchengesänge 1566

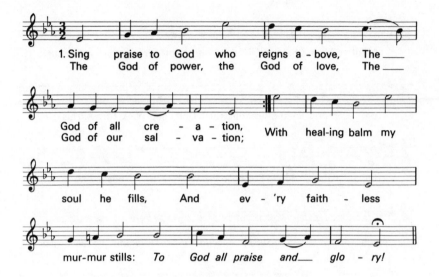

1. Sing praise to God who reigns a - bove, The____
The God of power, the God of love, The____

God of all cre - a - tion,
God of our sal - va - tion;

With heal-ing balm my

soul he fills, And ev - 'ry faith - less

mur-mur stills: *To God all praise and____ glo - ry!*

2 The angel-host, O King of kings,
    Thy praise for ever telling,
In earth and sky all living things
    Beneath thy shadow dwelling,
Adore the wisdom which could span
And power which formed creation's plan:

3 Then all my gladsome way along
    I sing aloud thy praises,
That men may hear the grateful song
    My voice unwearied raises:
Be joyful in the Lord, my heart!
Both soul and body bear your part!

4 O ye who name Christ's holy name,
    Give God all praise and glory:
All ye who own his power, proclaim
    Aloud the wondrous story!
Cast each false idol from his throne,
The Lord is God, and he alone:

J. J. Schutz 1640-1690 Tr. F. E. Cox

59

59
Soldiers of Christ, arise

From strength to strength

E. W. Naylor 1867-1934

1. Sol - diers of Christ, a - rise And put your ar - mour
on; Strong in the strength which God sup-plies, Through his e -
- ter - nal Son; Strong in the Lord of hosts, And in his
migh - ty power; Who in the strength of Je - sus
trusts Is more than · con - - - quer - or.

2 Stand then in his great might,
   With all his strength endued;
   But take, to arm you for the fight,
   The panoply of God;
   To keep your armour bright
   Attend with constant care,
   Still walking in your captain's sight,
   And watching unto prayer.

3 From strength to strength go on;
   Wrestle, and fight, and pray;
   Tread all the powers of darkness down,
   And win the well-fought day.
   That having all things done,
   And all your conflicts past,
   Ye may o'ercome, through Christ alone,
   And stand entire at last.

C. Wesley 1707-1788

60
Teach me, my God and King

Sandys

English traditional melody

1. Teach me, my God and King, In all things thee to see; And what I do in any-thing To do it as for thee!

2 A man that looks on glass,
 On it may stay his eye;
 Or if he pleaseth, through it pass,
 And then the heaven espy.

3 All may of thee partake;
 Nothing can be so mean,
 Which with this tincture, 'for thy sake,'
 Will not grow bright and clean.

4 A servant with this clause
 Makes drudgery divine;
 Who sweeps a room, as for thy laws,
 Makes that and the action fine.

5 This is the famous stone
 That turneth all to gold;
 For that which God doth touch and own
 Cannot for less be told.

G. Herbert 1593-1632

Arrangement for Soprano, Alto, Baritone

61
The Church of God a kingdom is

Capel

English traditional melody
Collected and arranged by L. E. Broadwood 1858-1929

1. The __ Church of __ God a __ king - dom is, Where

Christ in power doth reign, Where spir - its yearn till __

seen in bliss Their Lord shall come a - gain.

2 There rich and poor, from countless lands,
  Praise Christ on mystic rood;
  There nations reach forth holy hands
  To take God's holy food.

3 There pure life-giving streams o'erflow
  The sower's garden-ground;
  And faith and hope fair blossoms show,
  And fruits of love abound.

4 O King, O Christ, this endless grace
  To us and all men bring,
  To see the vision of thy face
  In joy, O Christ, our King.

L. B. C. L. Muirhead 1845-1925

62
The God of Abraham praise

Leoni

Hebrew melody, ad. Leoni

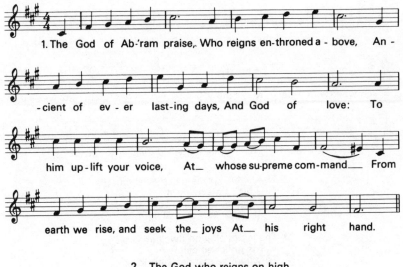

1. The God of Ab-'ram praise, Who reigns en-throned a - bove, An -
-cient of ev - er last-ing days, And God of love: To
him up-lift your voice, At_ whose su-preme com-mand_ From
earth we rise, and seek the_ joys At_ his right hand.

2 The God who reigns on high
The great archangels sing,
And 'Holy, holy, holy,' cry,
'Almighty King!'
Who was, and is, the same,
And evermore shall be:
Eternal Father, great "I am",
We worship thee.

T. Olivers 1725-1799

Arrangement for Soprano, Alto, Baritone

63
The head that once was crowned with thorns

Magnus   J. Clark 1670-1707

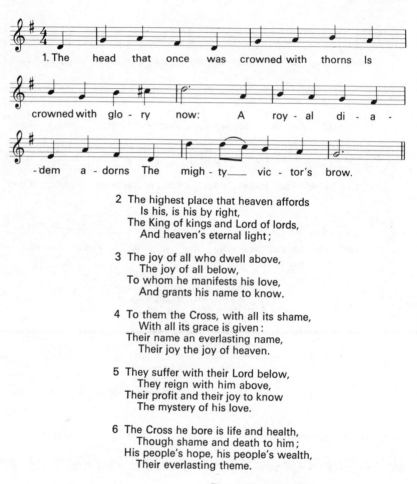

1. The head that once was crowned with thorns Is crowned with glo - ry now: A roy - al di - a - dem a - dorns The migh - ty_ vic - tor's brow.

2 The highest place that heaven affords
  Is his, is his by right,
  The King of kings and Lord of lords,
  And heaven's eternal light;

3 The joy of all who dwell above,
  The joy of all below,
  To whom he manifests his love,
  And grants his name to know.

4 To them the Cross, with all its shame,
  With all its grace is given:
  Their name an everlasting name,
  Their joy the joy of heaven.

5 They suffer with their Lord below,
  They reign with him above,
  Their profit and their joy to know
  The mystery of his love.

6 The Cross he bore is life and health,
  Though shame and death to him;
  His people's hope, his people's wealth,
  Their everlasting theme.

Thomas Kelly 1769-1854

Descant D. M-T.

64
The King of love my shepherd is

Dominus Regit Me

J. B. Dykes 1823-1876

1. The King of love my shep - herd is, Whose good - ness fail - eth nev - er; I noth - ing lack if I am his, And he is mine for ev - er.

2 Where streams of living water flow
   My ransom'd soul he leadeth,
   And where the verdant pastures grow
   With food celestial feedeth.

3 Perverse and foolish oft I stray'd,
   But yet in love he sought me,
   And on his shoulder gently laid,
   And home, rejoicing, brought me.

4 In death's dark vale I fear no ill
   With thee, dear Lord, beside me;
   Thy rod and staff my comfort still,
   Thy Cross before to guide me.

5 Thou spread'st a table in my sight;
   Thy unction grace bestoweth;
   And oh, what transport of delight
   From thy pure chalice floweth!

6 And so through all the length of days
   Thy goodness faileth never;
   Good Shepherd, may I sing thy praise
   Within thy house for ever.

Sir H. W. Baker 1821-1877

65
The Lord's my shepherd

Crimond

J. S. Irvine 1836-1887

1. The Lord's my shep - herd, I'll not want; He
makes me down to lie In pas - tures green; He
lead - eth me The qui - et wa - ters by.

2 My soul he doth restore again,
  And me to walk doth make
  Within the paths of righteousness
  E'en for his own name's sake.

3 Yea, though I walk in death's dark vale,
  Yet will I fear no ill;
  For thou art with me, and thy rod
  And staff me comfort still.

4 My table thou hast furnished
  In presence of my foes;
  My head thou dost with oil anoint
  And my cup overflows.

5 Goodness and mercy all my life
  Shall surely follow me;
  And in God's house for evermore
  My dwelling-place shall be.

W. Whittingham 1524-1579
F. Rous 1579-1659

66
These things shall be

Simeon   S. Stanley 1767-1822

1. These things shall be: a loft - ier race Than e'er the
world hath known shall rise, With flame of ___ free - dom ___
in their souls, And light of know - ledge ___ in their eyes.

2 They shall be gentle, brave, and strong
To spill no drop of blood, but dare
All that may plant man's lordship firm
On earth and fire and sea and air.

3 Nation with nation, land with land,
Unarmed shall live as comrades free;
In every heart and brain shall throb
The pulse of one fraternity.

4 Man shall love man, with heart as pure
And fervent as the young-eyed joys
Who chant their heavenly psalms before
God's face with undiscordant noise.

5 New arts shall bloom of loftier mould,
And mightier music thrill the skies,
And every life shall be a song,
When all the earth is paradise.

J. A. Symonds 1840-1893

67
Thou whose almighty word

Moscow

F. de Giardini 1716-1796

1. Thou whose al - migh - ty word Cha - os and

dark - ness heard, And took their flight;

Hear us, we humb - ly pray, And where the gos - pel day

Sheds not its glor - ious ray, Let there be light!

2 Thou who didst come to bring
   On thy redeeming wing
      Healing and sight,
   Health to the sick in mind,
   Sight to the inly blind,
   Ah! now to all mankind
      Let there be light!

3 Spirit of truth and love,
   Life-giving, holy dove,
      Speed forth thy flight!
   Move on the waters' face,
   Bearing the lamp of grace,
   And in earth's darkest place
      Let there be light!

4 Blessed and holy three,
   Glorious Trinity,
      Wisdom, love, might;
   Boundless as ocean tide
   Rolling in fullest pride,
   Through the world far and wide
      Let there be light!

J. Marriott 1780-1825

68
Through all the changing scenes of life

Wiltshire   G. Smart 1776-1867

1. Through all the chang - ing scenes_ of life, _ In trou - ble and_ in joy, _ The prais - es of my God_ shall still_ My _ heart and tongue_ em - ploy.

2 O magnify the Lord with me,
  With me exalt his name;
  When in distress to him I call'd,
  He to my rescue came.

3 The Hosts of God encamp around
  The dwellings of the just;
  Deliverance he affords to all
  Who on his succour trust.

4 O make but trial of his love, .
  Experience will decide
  How bless'd are they, and only they,
  Who in his truth confide.

5 Fear him, ye saints, and you will then
  Have nothing else to fear;
  Make you his service your delight,
  Your wants shall be his care.

6 To Father, Son and Holy Ghost,
  The God whom we adore,
  Be glory, as it was, is now,
  And shall be evermore.

N. Tate and N. Brady (1696)

69
Through the night of doubt and sorrow

Marching   Martin Shaw 1875-1958

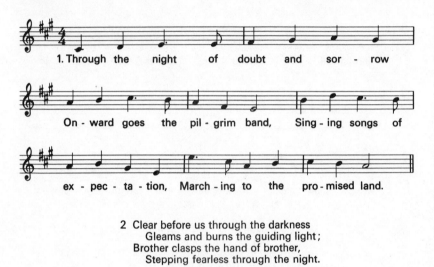

1. Through the night of doubt and sor - row
On - ward goes the pil - grim band, Sing - ing songs of
ex - pec - ta - tion, March - ing to the pro - mised land.

2 Clear before us through the darkness
   Gleams and burns the guiding light;
   Brother clasps the hand of brother,
   Stepping fearless through the night.

3 One the light of God's own presence
   O'er his ransomed people shed,
   Chasing far the gloom and terror,
   Brightening all the path we tread;

4 One the object of our journey,
   One the faith which never tires,
   One the earnest looking forward,
   One the hope our God inspires:

5 One the strain that lips of thousands
   Lift as from the heart of one;
   One the conflict, one the peril,
   One the march in God begun;

6 Onward, therefore, pilgrim brothers,
   Onward with the Cross our aid;
   Bear its shame, and fight its battle,
   Till we rest beneath its shade.

S. Baring Gould 1834-1924

70
Thy hand, O God, has guided

Thornbury   Basil Harwood 1859-1949

1. Thy hand, O God, has guid - ed Thy flock from age;_ to age; The won-d'rous tale is writ - ten, Full clear, on ev - 'ry page; Our fa - thers owned thy good - ness, And we_ their deeds re - cord; And both of_ these bear wit - ness, One Church, one faith, one Lord._____

2 Through many a day of darkness,
    Through many a scene of strife,
 The faithful few fought bravely
    To guard the nation's life.
 Their Gospel of redemption,
    Sin pardoned, man restored,
 Was all in this enfolded,
    One Church, one faith, one Lord.

3 And we, shall we be faithless?
    Shall hearts fail, hands hang down?
 Shall we evade. the conflict,
    And cast away our crown?
 Not so : in God's deep counsels
    Some better thing is stored ;
 We will maintain, unflinching,
    One Church, one faith, one Lord.

4 Thy mercy will not fail us,
    Nor leave thy work undone ;
 With thy right hand to help us,
    The victory shall be won ;
 And then, by men and angels,
    Thy name shall be adored,
 And this shall be their anthem,
    One Church, one faith, one Lord.

E. H. Plumptre 1821-1891

71
Thy kingdom come, O God

St. Cecilia

L. G. Hayne 1836-1883

1. Thy king-dom come, O God, Thy rule, O Christ be - gin; Break
with thine ir - on rod The ty - ran - nies of sin.

2 Where is thy reign of peace,
  And purity, and love?
When shall all hatred cease,
  As in the realms above?

3 When comes the promised time
  That war shall be no more—
Oppression, lust, and crime
  Shall flee thy face before?

4 We pray thee, Lord, arise,
  And come in thy great might;
Revive our longing eyes,
  Which languish for thy sight.

5 Men scorn thy sacred name,
  And wolves devour thy fold;
By many deeds of shame
  We learn that love grows cold.

6 O'er heathen lands afar
  Thick darkness broodeth yet:
Arise, O morning star,
  Arise, and never set!

L. Hensley 1824-1905

Arrangement for Soprano, Alto, Baritone

72
To the name that brings salvation

Oriel

C. Ett, *Cantica Sacra* 1846

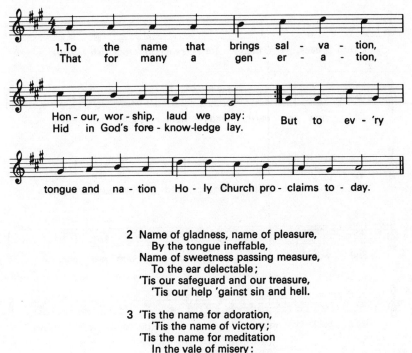

1. To the name that brings sal - va - tion,
That for many a gen - er - a - tion,

Hon - our, wor - ship, laud we pay:
Hid in God's fore - know-ledge lay.

But to ev - 'ry

tongue and na - tion Ho - ly Church pro - claims to - day.

2 Name of gladness, name of pleasure,
   By the tongue ineffable,
   Name of sweetness passing measure,
   To the ear delectable;
   'Tis our safeguard and our treasure,
   'Tis our help 'gainst sin and hell.

3 'Tis the name for adoration,
   'Tis the name of victory;
   'Tis the name for meditation
   In the vale of misery:
   'Tis the name for veneration
   By the citizens on high.

J. M. Neale 1818-1866

Descant Alan Gray

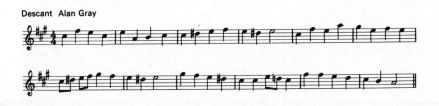

73

73
Turn back, O man

Old 124th

Genevan Psalter 1552

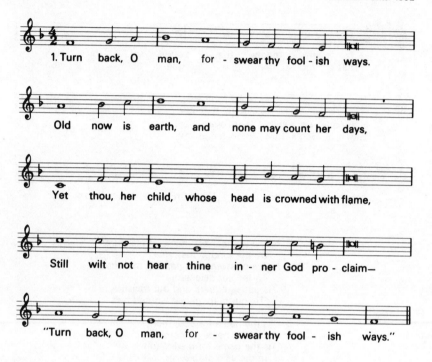

1. Turn back, O man, for - swear thy fool - ish ways.

Old now is earth, and none may count her days,

Yet thou, her child, whose head is crowned with flame,

Still wilt not hear thine in - ner God pro - claim—

"Turn back, O man, for - swear thy fool - ish ways."

2 Earth shall be fair, and all her people one:
Nor till that hour shall God's whole will be done;
Now, even now, once more from earth to sky,
Peals forth in joy man's old undaunted cry—
"Earth shall be fair, and all her folk be one."

C. Bax 1886-1962

74
When morning gilds the skies

Laudes Domini   Sir J. Barnby 1838-1896

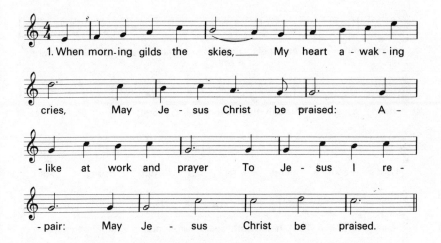

1. When morn-ing gilds the skies,___ My heart a - wak-ing cries, May Je - sus Christ be praised: A - like at work and prayer To Je - sus I re - pair: May Je - sus Christ be praised.

2 My tongue shall never tire
   Of chanting with the choir,
        May Jesus Christ be praised :
   This song of sacred joy,
   It never seems to cloy,
        May Jesus Christ be praised.

3 Does sadness fill my mind?
   A solace here I find,
        May Jesus Christ be praised :
   Or fades my earthly bliss?
   My comfort still is this,
        May Jesus Christ be praised.

4 The night becomes as day,
   When from the heart we say,
        May Jesus Christ be praised :
   The powers of darkness fear,
   When this sweet chant they hear,
        May Jesus Christ be praised.

5 Be this, while life is mine,
   My canticle divine,
        May Jesus Christ be praised :
   Be this the eternal song
   Through ages all along,
        May Jesus Christ be praised.

                                        E. Caswall 1814-1878

75
Ye holy angels bright

Darwall's 148th

J. Darwall 1731-1789

1. Ye ho - ly an - gels bright, Who wait at God's right hand, Or through the realms of light Fly at your Lord's com - mand, As - sist our song, For else the theme Too high doth seem For mor - tal tongue.

2 Ye blessed souls at rest,
   Who ran this earthly race,
   And now, from sin released,
   Behold the Saviour's face;
   God's praises sound,
   As in his sight
   With sweet delight
   Ye do abound.

3 Ye saints, who toil below,
   Adore your heavenly King,
   And onward as ye go
   Some joyful anthem sing;
   Take what he gives
   And praise him still,
   Through good or ill,
   Who ever lives!

4 My soul, bear thou thy part,
   Triumph in God above:
   And with a well-tuned heart
   Sing thou the songs of love!
   Let all thy days
   Till life shall end,
   Whate'er he send,
   Be filled with praise.

R. Baxter (1681) and J. H. Gurney (1838)

Descant D. M-T.

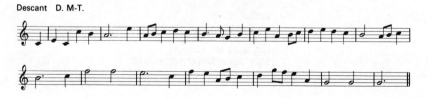

76
Ye servants of God, your Master proclaim

Paderborn   *Paderborn Gesangbuch* 1765

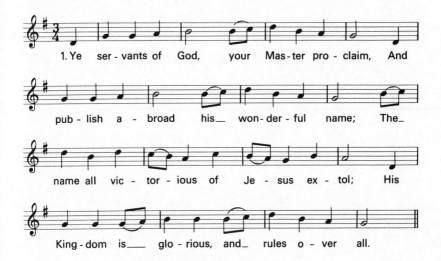

1. Ye ser-vants of God, your Mas-ter pro-claim, And pub-lish a-broad his__ won-der-ful name; The__ name all vic-tor-ious of Je-sus ex-tol; His King-dom is__ glo-rious, and__ rules o-ver all.

2 God ruleth on high, almighty to save;
And still he is nigh; his presence we have.
The great congregation his triumph shall sing,
Ascribing salvation to Jesus our King.

3 "Salvation to God who sits on the throne!"
Let all cry aloud, and honour the Son.
The praises of Jesus the angels proclaim,
Fall down on their faces, and worship the lamb.

4 Then let us adore, and give him his right:
All glory and power, all wisdom and might,
All honour and blessing, with angels above,
And thanks never-ceasing, and infinite love.

C. Wesley 1707-1788

HYMNS FOR SPECIAL OCCASIONS

Advent	77, 78, 79
Christmas	80, 81, 82, 83, 84, 85, 86
Epiphany	87, 88
Easter	89, 90, 91, 92, 93
Harvest	94, 95, 96, 97
National	98, 99, 100, 101, 102
The Lord's Prayer	103

77
Hark the glad sound

Bristol

Ravenscroft's Psalter 1621

1. Hark the glad sound! the Sa - viour comes, The
Sa - viour pro - mised long! Let ev - 'ry heart pre -
- pare a throne, And ev - 'ry voice a song.

2 He comes the prisoners to release
   In Satan's bondage held;
   The gates of brass before him burst,
   The iron fetters yield.

3 He comes the broken heart to bind,
   The bleeding soul to cure,
   And with the treasures of his grace
   To enrich the humble poor.

4 Our glad hosannas, Prince of peace,
   Thy welcome shall proclaim;
   And heaven's eternal arches ring
   With thy beloved name.

P. Doddridge 1702-1751

Descant   D. M-T.

78
Lo, he comes with clouds descending

Helmsley   18th Century English melody

1. Lo, he___ comes with___ clouds___ de - scend - ing,
Thous - and___ thous - and___ saints___ at - tend - ing

Once for fav - our'd sin - ners___ slain;___
Swell the tri - umph of___ his___ train:___

Al - le - lu - ia, Al - le - lu - ia, Al - le -

- lu - ia, Christ ap - pears on earth a - gain.

2 Every eye shall now behold him
  Robed in dreadful majesty;
Those who set at nought and sold him
  Pierced and nail'd him to the Tree,
    Deeply wailing,
  Shall the true Messiah see.

3 Those dear tokens of his Passion
  Still his dazzling body bears,
Cause of endless exultation
  To his ransom'd worshippers;
    With what rapture
  Gaze we on those glorious scars!

4 Yea, Amen, let all adore thee,
  High on thine eternal throne;
Saviour, take the power and glory;
  Claim the kingdom for thine own:
    Alleluia!
  Thou shalt reign, and thou alone.

C. Wesley 1707-1788

79

O come, O come, Emmanuel

Veni Emmanuel

From "A French Missal"
melody adapted by T. Helmore
and arranged by J. H. Arnold 1887-1956

1. O come, O come, Em - man - u - el! Re-deem thy cap-tive Is - ra-el, That in - to ex - ile drear __ is gone Far from the face of God's __ dear Son. Re-joice! Re-joice! Em - man - u - el Shall come to thee, O Is - ra - el.

2 O come, O come, thou dayspring bright!
Pour on our souls thy healing light;
Dispel the long night's lingering gloom,
And pierce the shadows of the tomb.

3 O come, thou Lord of David's Key!
The royal door fling wide and free;
Safeguard for us the heavenward road,
And bar the way to death's abode.

18th Century, Tr. T. A. Lacey 1853-1931

80
Hark! the herald angels sing

Mendelssohn

F. Mendelssohn–Bartholdy 1809-1847

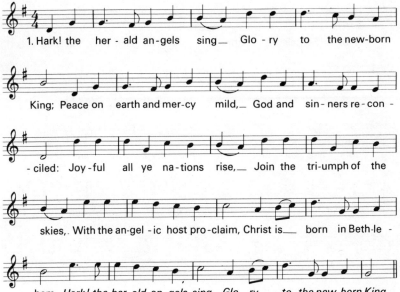

1. Hark! the her-ald an-gels sing— Glo-ry to the new-born
King; Peace on earth and mer-cy mild,— God and sin-ners re-con-
-ciled: Joy-ful all ye na-tions rise,— Join the tri-umph of the
skies,. With the an-gel-ic host pro-claim, Christ is— born in Beth-le-
-hem. *Hark! the her-ald an-gels sing Glo-ry— to the new-born King.*

2 Christ, by highest heaven adored,
Christ, the everlasting Lord,
Late in time behold him come,
Offspring of a virgin's womb!
Veiled in flesh the Godhead see,
Hail the incarnate Deity!
Pleased as man with man to dwell,
Jesus, our Emmanuel.

3 Hail the heaven-born Prince of peace!
Hail the Sun of Righteousness!
Light and life to all he brings,
Risen with healing in his wings;
Mild he lays his glory by,
Born that man no more may die,
Born to raise the sons of earth,
Born to give them second birth.

C. Wesley 1707-1788 and others

81
O come, all ye faithful

Adeste Fideles

J. F. Wade's MS. Book

1. O come, all ye faith - ful, Joy-ful and tri - um-phant, O
come ye, O come_ ye to Beth - le - hem;
Come and be - hold him, Born the King of an - gels: O
come, let us a - dore him, O come, let us a - dore him, O
come, let us a - dore him, __ Christ__ the Lord!

2   God of God,
       Light of Light,
   Lo! he abhors not the virgin's womb;
       Very God,
       Begotten not created:

3   Sing, choirs of angels,
       Sing in exultation,
   Sing, all ye citizens of heaven above,
       Glory to God
       In the highest:

Tr. F. Oakeley 1802-1880

Descant   D. M-T.

O come_ O come let us a - dore_ him_ Christ the Lord.

82
O little town of Bethlehem

Forest Green

Arranged by R. Vaughan Williams 1872-1958
from an English traditional melody

1. O lit - tle town of Beth - le - hem, How still we_ see thee lie! A - bove thy deep and dream - less_ sleep The si - lent_ stars go by. Yet_ in thy dark_ streets shi - neth The ev - er - last - ing light; The hopes and fears of all_ the_ years Are met in_ thee to - night.

2 O morning stars, together
  Proclaim the holy birth,
And praises sing to God the King,
  And peace to men on earth;
For Christ is born of Mary;
  And, gathered all above,
While mortals sleep, the angels keep
  Their watch of wondering love.

3 How silently, how silently,
  The wondrous gift is given!
So God imparts to human hearts
  The blessings of his heaven.
No ear may hear his coming;
  But in this world of sin,
Where meek souls will receive him, still
  The dear Christ enters in.

4 Where children pure and happy
  Pray to the blessed Child,
Where misery cries out to thee,
  Son of the mother mild;
Where charity stands watching
  And faith holds wide the door,
The dark night wakes, the glory breaks,
  And Christmas comes once more.

P. Brooks 1835-1893

83
Once in royal David's city

Irby

H. J. Gauntlett 1805-1876

1. Once in roy - al Da - vid's __ ci - ty Stood a low - ly cat - tle __ shed Where a mo - ther laid __ her __ ba - by In a man - ger for __ his __ bed, Ma - ry was that mo - ther mild, Je - sus Christ her lit - tle __ child.

2 He came down to earth from heaven,
   Who is God and Lord of all,
And his shelter was a stable,
   And his cradle was a stall;
With the poor and mean, and lowly,
Lived on earth our Saviour holy.

3 And through all his wondrous childhood
   He would honour and obey,
   Love and watch the lowly maiden,
     In whose gentle arms he lay:
   Christian children all must be
   Mild, obedient, good as he.

4 And our eyes at last shall see him,
    Through his own redeeming love,
   For that child so dear and gentle
    Is our Lord in heaven above;
   And he leads his children on
   To the place where he is gone.

Mrs. C. F. Alexander 1818-1895

Arrangement for Soprano, Alto, Baritone

87

84
The first Nowell

The First Nowell

English traditional melody

1. The first Now-ell the an-gel did say, Was to
In fields where they lay a-keep-ing their sheep On a

cer-tain poor shep-herds in fields as they lay;
cold win-ter's night that was so deep:

Now-ell, Now-ell, Now-ell, Now-ell,

Born is the King of Is - ra - el.

2 They looked up and saw a star,
Shining in the east, beyond them far,
And to the earth it gave great light,
And so it continued both day and night:

3 And by the light of that same star,
Three wise men came from country far;
To seek for a king was their intent,
And to follow the star wherever it went:

4 This star drew nigh to the north-west,
O'er Bethlehem it took its rest,
And there it did both stop and stay
Right over the place where Jesus lay:

5 Then entered in those wise men three,
Full reverently upon their knee,
And offered there in his presence
Their gold and myrrh and frankincense:

6 Then let us all with one accord
Sing praises to our heavenly Lord,
That hath made heaven and earth of nought,
And with his blood mankind hath bought:

Traditional

85
Unto us a boy is born

Puer Nobis

Piae Cantiones

1. Un - to us a boy is born, King of all cre - a - tion: Came he to a world for - lorn, The Lord of ev - 'ry na - tion, the Lord of ev - 'ry na - tion.

2 Cradled in a stall was he,
  With sleepy cows and asses;
But the very beasts could see
  That he all men surpasses.

3 Herod then with fear was filled:
  'A Prince,' he said, 'in Jewry!'
All the little boys he killed
  At Bethlem in his fury.

4 Now may Mary's son, who came
  So long ago to love us,
Lead us all with hearts aflame
  Unto the joys above us.

5 Omega and Alpha he!
  Let the organ thunder,
While the choir with peals of glee
  Doth rend the air asunder.

Tr. P. Dearmer 1867-1936

86
While shepherds watched

Winchester Old

Este's Psalter 1592

1. While shep - herds watched their flocks by night, All
seat - ed on the ground, The an - gel of the
Lord came down, And glo - ry shone a - round.

2 'Fear not,' said he (for mighty dread
  Had seized their troubled mind) ;
  'Glad tidings of great joy I bring
  To you and all mankind.

3 'To you in David's town this day
  Is born of David's line
  A saviour, who is Christ the Lord ;
  And this shall be the sign :

4 'The heavenly babe you there shall find
  To human view displayed,
  All meanly wrapped in swathing bands
  And in a manger laid.'

5 Thus spake the seraph ; and forthwith
  Appeared a shining throng
  Of angels praising God, who thus
  Addressed their joyful song :

6 'All glory be to God on high,
  And to the earth be peace ;
  Good will henceforth from heaven to men
  Begin and never cease.'

Nahum Tate 1652-1715

87
As with gladness men of old

Dix

C. Kocher 1786-1872

1. As with glad-ness men of old   Did the guid-ing star be-hold,

As with joy they hailed its light,   Lead-ing on-ward, beam-ing bright,

So, most gra-cious God, may we   Ev - er - more be led to thee.

2 As with joyful steps they sped
  To that lowly manger-bed,
  There to bend the knee before
  Him whom heaven and earth adore,
  So may we with willing feet
  Ever seek thy mercy-seat.

3 As they offered gifts most rare
  At that manger rude and bare,
  So may we with holy joy,
  Pure, and free from sin's alloy,
  All our costliest treasures bring,
  Christ, to thee our heavenly King.

4 Holy Jesu, every day
  Keep us in the narrow way;
  And, when earthly things are past,
  Bring our ransomed souls at last
  Where they need no star to guide,
  Where no clouds thy glory hide.

5 In the heavenly country bright
  Need they no created light;
  Thou its light, its joy, its crown,
  Thou its sun which goes not down:
  There for ever may we sing
  Alleluyas to our King.

W. C. Dix 1837-1898

91

88
Bethlehem, of noblest cities

Stuttgart

Psalmodia Sacra 1715
adapted by C. F. Witt c. 1660-1716

1. Beth - le - hem, of nob - lest cit - ies
None can once with thee com - pare; Thou a - lone the
Lord from heav - en Didst for us in - carn - ate bear.

2 Fairer than the sun at morning
   Was the star that told his birth;
To the lands their God announcing,
   Hid beneath a form of earth.

3 By its lambent beauty guided
   See the eastern kings appear;
See them bend, their gifts to offer,
   Gifts of incense, gold and myrrh.

4 Solemn things of mystic meaning:
   Incense doth the God disclose,
Gold a royal child proclaimeth,
   Myrrh a future tomb foreshows.

5 Holy Jesu, in thy brightness
   To the Gentile world displayed,
With the Father and the Spirit
   Endless praise to thee be paid.

Tr. E. Caswall 1814-1878

89
In the Cross of Christ I glory

Wychbold   W. G. Whinfield 1865-1919

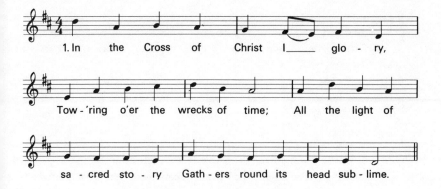

1. In the Cross of Christ I____ glo - ry,
Tow - 'ring o'er the wrecks of time; All the light of
sa - cred sto - ry Gath - ers round its head sub - lime.

2 When the woes of life o'ertake me,
    Hopes deceive and fears annoy,
  Never shall the Cross forsake me,
    Lo! it glows with peace and joy.

3 When the sun of bliss is beaming
    Light and love upon my way,
  From the Cross the radiance streaming
    Adds more lustre to the day.

4 Bane and blessing, pain and pleasure,
    By the Cross are sanctified;
  Peace is there that knows no measure,
    Joys that through all time abide.

J. Bowring 1792-1872

90
Ride on, ride on in majesty

St. Droṣtane

J. B. Dykes 1823-1876

1. Ride on, ride on in ma - jes - ty! Hark! all the tribes 'Ho - san - na' cry; O Sav - iour meek, pur - sue thy road with palms and scat - tered gar - ments strowed.

2 Ride on, ride on in majesty!
In lowly pomp ride on to die;
O Christ, thy triumphs now begin
O'er captive death and conquered sin.

3 Ride on, ride on in majesty!
The winged squadrons of the sky
Look down with sad and wondering eyes
To see the approaching sacrifice.

4 Ride on, ride on in majesty!
Thy last and fiercest strife is nigh;
The Father on his sapphire throne,
Expects his own anointed Son.

5 Ride on, ride on in majesty!
In lowly pomp ride on to die;
Bow thy meek head to mortal pain,
Then take, O God, thy power, and reign.

H. H. Milman 1791-1868

91
There is a green hill far away

Horsley   W. Horsley 1774-1858

1. There is a green hill far a - way, With -
out a ci - ty wall, Where the dear Lord was
cru - ci - fied, Who died to save us all.

2 We may not know, we cannot tell,
 What pains he had to bear,
But we believe it was for us
 He hung and suffered there.

3 O, dearly, dearly has he loved,
 And we must love him too,
And trust in his redeeming blood
 And try his works to do.

Mrs. C. F. Alexander 1818-1895

92
Thine be the glory

Maccabaeus

G. F. Handel 1685-1759

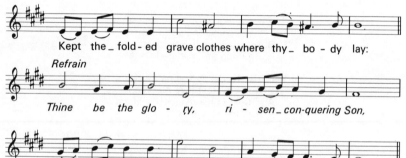

1. Thine be the glo - ry, ri - sen_ con-quering Son;
End - less is the vic - t'ry thou o'er death hast won:
An - gels in bright rai - ment rolled the stone a - way,
Kept the _ fold - ed grave clothes where thy _ bo - dy lay:

Refrain

Thine be the glo - ry, ri - sen_ con-quering Son,
End - less is the vic - t'ry thou o'er death hast won.

2 Lo! Jesus meets us, risen from the tomb;
Lovingly he greets us, scatters fear and gloom;
Let the Church with gladness hymns of triumph sing;
For her Lord now liveth; death hath lost its sting:
Thine be the glory, risen, conquering Son,
Endless is the victory thou o'er death hast won.

3 No more we doubt thee, glorious Prince of Life;
Life is nought without thee; aid us in our strife;
Make us more than conquerors, through thy deathless love;
Bring us safe through Jordan to thy home above;
Thine be the glory, risen, conquering Son,
Endless is the victory thou o'er death hast won.

R. B. Hoyle 1875-1939

93
When I survey the wondrous Cross

Rockingham

ad. E. Miller 1731-1807

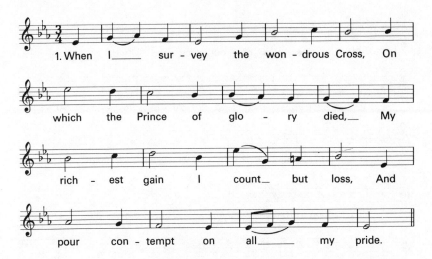

1. When I___ sur-vey the won-drous Cross, On which the Prince of glo-ry died,___ My rich-est gain I count___ but loss, And pour con-tempt on all___ my pride.

2 Forbid it, Lord, that I should boast,
   Save in the death of Christ my God ;
All the vain things that charm me most,
   I sacrifice them to his blood.

3 See from his head, his hands, his feet,
   Sorrow and love flow mingled down ;
Did e'er such love and sorrow meet,
   Or thorns compose so rich a crown ?

4 Were the whole realm of nature mine,
   That were an offering far too small ;
Love so amazing, so divine,
   Demands my soul, my life, my all.

I. Watts 1674-1748

94
All creatures of our God and King

Lasst uns Erfreuen

Kirchengesang, 1623

1. All crea-tures of our God and King, Lift up your voice and with us sing Al - le - lu - ia, Al - le - lu - ia! Thou burn-ing sun with gold-en beam, Thou sil-ver moon with soft - er gleam, O___ praise him, O ___ praise him, Al -le - lu - ia, Al -le - lu - ia, Al -le - lu - ia!

2 Thou rushing wind that art so strong,
Ye clouds that sail in heaven along,
  O praise him, Alleluia!
Thou rising morn, in praise rejoice,
Ye lights of evening, find a voice:
  O praise him, O praise him,
  Alleluia, Alleluia, Alleluia!

3 Thou flowing water, pure and clear,
Make music for thy Lord to hear,
  Alleluia, Alleluia!
Thou fire so masterful and bright,
That givest man both warmth and light:
  O praise him, O praise him,
  Alleluia, Alleluia, Alleluia!

4 Dear mother earth, who day by day
Unfoldest blessings on our way,
  O praise him, Alleluia!
The flowers and fruits that in thee grow,
Let them his glory also show:
  O praise him, O praise him,
  Alleluia, Alleluia, Alleluia!

5 Let all things their Creator bless,
And worship him in humbleness,
  O praise him, Alleluia!
Praise, praise the Father, praise the Son,
And praise the Spirit, Three in One;
  O praise him, O praise him,
  Alleluia, Alleluia, Alleluia!

St. Francis, Tr. W. H. Draper 1855-1933

95
All things praise thee, Lord most high

Te Laudant Omnia   J. F. Swift 1847-1931

1. All things praise thee, Lord most high: Heaven, and earth, and sea, and sky, All were for thy glo - ry made, That thy great-ness, thus dis - played, Should all_ wor - ship bring to_ thee; All things praise thee: Lord may we!

2 All things praise thee: night to night
  Sings in silent hymns of light;
  All things praise thee; day to day
  Chants thy power in burning ray;
  Time and space are praising thee;
  All things praise thee: Lord may we!

3 All things praise thee: high and low,
  Rain, and dew, and seven-hued bow,
  Crimson sunset, fleecy cloud,
  Rippling stream, and tempest loud;
  Summer, winter, all to thee
  Glory render: Lord may we!

4 All things praise thee: gracious Lord,
  Great Creator, powerful Word,
  Omnipresent Spirit, now
  At thy feet we humbly bow;
  Lift our hearts in praise to thee;
  All things praise thee: Lord may we!

                          G. W. Conder 1821-1874

96
Come, ye thankful people, come

St. George

G. F. Elvey 1816-1893

1. Come, ye thank-ful peo-ple, come, Raise the song of
har-vest-home! All be safe-ly gath-ered in,
Ere the win-ter storms be-gin;
God, our Ma-ker, doth pro-vide For our wants to
be sup-plied; Come to God's own tem-ple, come;
Raise the song of har-vest-home!

2 We ourselves are God's own field,
Fruit unto his praise to yield;
Wheat and tares together sown,
Unto joy or sorrow grown;
First the blade and then the ear,
Then the full corn shall appear:
Grant, O harvest Lord, that we
Wholesome grain and pure may be.

3 For the Lord our God shall come,
And shall take his harvest home;
From his field shall in that day
All offences purge away;
Give his angels charge at last
In the fire the tares to cast;
But the fruitful ears to store
In his garner evermore.

H. Alford 1810-1871

100

97
Praise, O praise our God and King

Monkland

J. B. Wilkes 1785-1869

1. Praise, O praise our God and King! Hymns of a-dor-a-tion sing; For his mer-cies still en-dure, Ev-er faith-ful, ev-er sure.

2 Praise him that he made the sun
Day by day his course to run:
For his mercies still endure
Ever faithful, ever sure.

3 And the silver moon by night,
Shining with her gentle light:
For his mercies still endure
Ever faithful, ever sure.

4 Praise him that he gave the rain
To mature the swelling grain:
For his mercies still endure
Ever faithful, ever sure.

5 And hath bid the fruitful field
Crops of precious increase yield:
For his mercies still endure
Ever faithful, ever sure.

6 Praise him for our harvest-store;
He hath filled the garner-floor:
For his mercies still endure
Ever faithful, ever sure.

7 And for richer food than this,
Pledge of everlasting bliss:
For his mercies still endure
Ever faithful, ever sure.

8 Glory to our bounteous King;
Glory let creation sing:
Glory to the Father, Son,
And blest Spirit, Three in One.

Sir H. W. Baker 1821-1877

Arrangement for Soprano, Alto, Baritone

98
And did those feet in ancient time

Jerusalem

Sir C. Hubert H. Parry 1848-1918

And did those feet in an - cient time Walk up-on England's moun - tains green? And was the ho - ly Lamb of __ God On England's pleas-ant past - ures seen? And did the coun - ten-ance div - ine Shine forth up - on our cloud-ed hills? And was Je - ru - sa-lem build - ed here A-mong those dark Sa-tan - ic mills?

Bring me my bow of burn - ing_ gold! Bring me my ar -rows of de - sire! Bring me my spear! O clouds un - fold! Bring me my cha - ri - ot of fire! I will not cease from men - tal fight, Nor shall my sword sleep in my hand Till we have built Je - ru - sa - lem In Eng-land's green and pleas - ant land.

Stanzas from Blake's "Prophetic Books"
William Blake 1757-18 27

102

I vow to thee, my country

Thaxted

Gustav Holst 1874-1934

1. I___ vow to thee, my coun - try, all earth-ly things a -
-bove, En - tire and whole and per - fect, the
ser - vice of my love, The___ love that asks no
quest - ion, the___ love that stands the test, That___
lays up - on the al - tar the dear - est and the
best; The___ love that nev - er fal - ters, the
love that pays the price, The___ love that makes un -
- daunt - ed the fin - al sa - cri - fice.

2 And there's another country, I've heard of long ago,
   Most dear to them that love her, most great to them that know;
   We may not count her armies; we may not see her king;
   Her fortress is a faithful heart, her pride is suffering;
   And soul by soul and silently her shining bounds increase,
   And her ways are ways of gentleness and all her paths are peace.

Sir Cecil Spring-Rice 1859-1918

100
Lord, while for all mankind we pray

Tallis' Ordinal

Thomas Tallis c. 1510-1585

1. Lord, while for all man - kind we pray Of ev - 'ry clime and coast, O hear us for our na - tive land, The land we love the most.

2 O guard our shores from every foe;
    With peace our borders bless;
    With prosperous times our cities crown,
    Our fields with plenteousness.

3 Unite us in the sacred love
    Of knowledge, truth and thee;
    And let our hills and valleys shout
    The songs of liberty.

4 Lord of the nations, thus to thee
    Our country we commend;
    Be thou her refuge and her trust,
    Her everlasting friend.

J. R. Wreford 1800-1881

101
O God, our help in ages past

St. Anne

W. Croft 1671-1727

1. O God, our help in a - ges past, Our hope for years to come, Our shel - ter from the storm - y blast, And our e - ter - nal home;

2 Under the shadow of thy throne
  Thy saints have dwelt secure;
  Sufficient is thine arm alone,
  And our defence is sure.

3 Before the hills in order stood,
  Or earth received her frame,
  From everlasting thou art God,
  To endless years the same.

4 A thousand ages in thy sight
  Are like an evening gone,
  Short as the watch that ends the night
  Before the rising sun.

5 Time, like an ever-rolling stream,
  Bears all its sons away;
  They fly forgotten, as a dream
  Dies at the opening day.

6 O God, our help in ages past,
  Our hope for years to come,
  Be thou our guard while troubles last,
  And our eternal home.

I. Watts 1674-1748

Descant Martin Shaw 1875-1958

105

102
The National Anthem

Gentleman's Magazine 1745

God save our gra - cious Queen, Long live our

no - ble Queen, God save the Queen!

Send her vic - tor - i - ous, Hap - py and glor - i - ous,

Long to— reign ov - er us, God— save the Queen.

2 One realm of races four,
Blest more and ever more,
God save our land !
Home of the brave and free,
Set in the silver sea,
True nurse of chivalry,
God save our land !

3 Of many a race and birth
From utmost ends of earth,
God save us all !
Bid strife and hatred cease,
Bid hope and joy increase,
Spread universal peace,
God save us all !

National Anthem

103
The Lord's Prayer

St. Flavian

Psalmes 1562

1. Our Fa - ther, God, Who art in heav'n, All hal - lowed be thy name; Thy king - dom come; thy will be done, In earth and heav'n the same. A - men.

2 Give us this day our daily bread;
And as we those forgive
Who sin against us, so may we
Forgiving grace receive.

3 Into temptation lead us not;
From evil set us free;
And thine the kingdom, thine the power
And glory ever be.

Adoniram Judson 1788-1850

107

INDEX OF FIRST LINES
ARRANGED ALPHABETICALLY

Hymn No.	First Line	Tune	Page
1	A charge to keep I have	Carlisle	1
2	A safe stronghold our God is still	Ein' Feste Burg	2
94	All creatures of our God and King	Lasst uns Erfreuen	98
3	All hail the power of Jesu's name	Miles Lane	3
4	All people that on earth do dwell	Old Hundredth	4
95	All things praise thee, Lord most high	Te Laudant Omnia	99
98	And did those feet in ancient time	Jerusalem	102
5	Angel voices ever singing	Angel voices	5
87	As with gladness men of old	Dix	91
6	At the name of Jesus	King's Weston	6
88	Bethlehem, of noblest cities	Stuttgart	92
7	Blest are the pure in heart	Franconia	7
8	City of God, how broad and far	Richmond	8
10	Come down, O love divine (SAB)	Down Ampney	10
9	Come, let us join our cheerful songs	Cheerful	9
11	Come, ye faithful raise the anthem (D)	Neander	12
96	Come, ye thankful people, come	St. George	100
12	Dear Lord and Father of mankind	Repton	13
13	Father, hear the prayer we offer	Gott Will's Machen	14
14	Fight the good fight with all thy might (D)	Duke Street	15
15	Fill thou my life, O Lord my God	St. Fulbert	16
16	For all the Saints who from their labours rest	Sine Nomine	17
17	For the beauty of the earth	England's Lane	18
18	Forth in thy name, O Lord, I go (SAB)	Angel's Song	19
19	Glad that I live am I	Water-End	20
20	Glorious things of thee are spoken	Austrian Hymn	21
21	God is love, his mercy brightens	Sussex	22
102	God save our gracious Queen	National Anthem	106
22	Guide me, O thou great Redeemer	Cwm Rhondda	23
23	Hail to the Lord's anointed	Cruger	24
77	Hark the glad sound, the Saviour comes (D)	Bristol	82
80	Hark! the herald angels sing	Mendelssohn	85
24	He who would valiant be	Monks Gate	25
25	Hills of the North, rejoice	Little Cornard	26
26	How sweet the name of Jesus sounds (SAB)	St. Peter	27
99	I vow to thee, my country, all earthly things above	Thaxted	103

Hymn

No.	First Line	Tune	Page
27	Immortal, invisible, God only wise	St. Denio	28
28	In Christ there is no east or west	St. Bernard	29
89	In the cross of Christ I glory	Wychbold	93
29	It is a thing most wonderful	Herongate	30
30	Jesus, good above all other	Quem pastores laudavere	31
31	Jesus shall reign where'er the sun	Truro	32
32	Judge eternal, throned in splendour (D)	Rhuddlan	33
33	King of Glory, King of Peace	Gwalchmai	34
34	Lamb of God, I look to thee	Vienna	35
35	Lead us, heavenly Father, lead us (SAB)	Mannheim	36
36	Let all the world in every corner sing	Luckington	37
37	Lift up your hearts, we lift them Lord to thee	Woodlands	38
78	Lo, he comes with clouds descending	Helmsley	81
38	Lord of all being, throned afar	Maryton	39
39	Lord of all hopefulness, Lord of all joy	Slane	40
100	Lord, while for all mankind we pray	Tallis' Ordinal	104
40	Love divine, all loves excelling (SAB)	Love divine	41
41	Mine eyes have seen the glory of the coming of the Lord	Vision	42
42	Morning has broken	Bunessan	43
43	My God, my King	Warwick	44
44	My heart and voice I raise	Ascalon	45
45	My song is love unknown	Love unknown	46
46	New every morning is the love (D)	Melcombe	47
47	Now thank we all our God	Nun Danket	48
81	O come, all ye faithful (D)	Adeste Fideles	84
79	O come, O come, Emmanuel	Veni Emmanuel	82
48	O for a thousand tongues to sing	Halifax	49
101	O God, our help in ages past (D)	St. Anne	105
49	O Jesus, I have promised	Day of Rest	50
82	O little town of Bethlehem	Forest Green	85
50	O praise ye the Lord	Laudate Dominum	51
52	O worship the King	Hanover	53
83	Once in royal David's city (SAB)	Irby	86
51	Onward, Christian soldiers	St. Gertrude	52
103	Our Father, God, who art in heav'n	St. Flavian	107
54	Praise, my soul, the King of Heaven	Praise my soul	55
97	Praise, O praise our God and King (SAB)	Monkland	101
53	Praise to the holiest in the height	Gerontius	54
55	Praise to the Lord, the almighty	Praxis Pietatis	56
56	Rejoice, the Lord is King	Gopsal	57
90	Ride on, ride on in majesty	St. Drostane	94
57	Saviour, while my heart is tender	Shipston	58
58	Sing praise to God who reigns above	Mit Freuden Zart	59

Hymn No.	First Line	Tune	Page
59	Soldiers of Christ, arise	From strength to strength	60
60	Teach me, my God and King (SAB)	Sandys	61
61	The Church of God a Kingdom is	Capel	62
84	The first Nowell the angel did say	The first Nowell	88
62	The God of Abraham praise (SAB)	Leoni	63
63	The Head that once was crowned with thorns (D)	Magnus	64
64	The King of love my shepherd is	Dominus regit me	65
65	The Lord's my shepherd, I'll not want	Crimond	66
91	There is a green hill far away	Horsley	95
66	These things shall be	Simeon	67
92	Thine be the glory, risen conquering son	Maccabaeus	96
67	Thou whose almighty word	Moscow	68
68	Through all the changing scenes of life	Wiltshire	69
69	Through the night of doubt and sorrow	Marching	70
70	Thy hand, O God, has guided	Thornbury	71
71	Thy Kingdom come, O God (SAB)	St. Cecilia	72
72	To the name that brings salvation (D)	Oriel	73
73	Turn back, O man, foreswear thy foolish ways	Old 124th	74
85	Unto us a boy is born	Puer Nobis	89
93	When I survey the wondrous cross	Rockingham	97
74	When morning gilds the skies	Laudes Domini	75
86	While shepherds watched their flocks by night	Winchester Old	90
75	Ye holy angels bright (D)	Darwall's 148th	76
76	Ye servants of God, your master proclaim	Paderborn	77